Beat Dyslexia

A step-by-step
multi-sensory literacy programme

Elizabeth Franks • Myra Nicholson • Celia Stone

The handwriting script used in this publication is available as a stand-alone product. *Handwriting for Windows* is available from www.kber.co.uk and from LDA.

This pack contains:
    Beat Dyslexia Book 5 – Photocopiable resource book
    Audio CD
    31 Reading and Spelling Cards

Additional copies of the audio CD and packs of the Reading and Spelling Cards are available. Please contact our Customer Services Team on 0845 120 4776.

The rights of Liz Franks, Celia Stone and Myra Nicholson to be identified as the authors of this work have been asserted by them in accordance with sections 77 and 78 of the Copyright, Designs and Patents Act 1988.

Permission has been sought for the inclusion of all copyright material in this book. Apologies are offered to any copyright holder whom it has not been possible to contact. Omissions should be notified to the publisher and will be rectified in subsequent editions.

Beat Dyslexia Book 5
100794
ISBN-13: 978 1 85503 474 7
© Liz Franks, Celia Stone and Myra Nicholson
Illustrations © Garry Davies and Simon Rumble
Voice: Dan Strauss
All rights reserved
First published 1997
Second edition published 2009

Printed in China for LDA
Pintail Close, Victoria Business Park, Nottingham, NG4 2SG

Contents

Preface

The new edition of *Beat Dyslexia* reflects considerable experience in the teaching of dyslexic pupils. This updated series promises to develop literacy skills by combining successful phonological approaches with the very best of conventional, multi-sensory, structured teaching methods.

The *Beat Dyslexia* books are designed primarily for dyslexic pupils of all ages, but the careful use of visual and aural approaches, in a clearly structured progression, makes them very suitable for any pupil who may be struggling to acquire literacy skills. The series has been designed to take pupils from the earliest stages of letter recognition through to full literacy. On completion of Books 1, 2 and 3, the pupil will have achieved mastery of the elements required for Key Stage 1 of the National Curriculum. Books 4 and 5 aim to support pupils to Key Stage 2 and through the early years of secondary school.

Recognising the need to engage the pupil's concentration, the authors have made the activities and exercises both varied and entertaining. The teacher or tutor is enabled to measure attainment by a progressive series of engaging reading passages and spelling tests.

We wish all success and enjoyment to pupils using these books. You will have the reward of making steady progress as you advance from book to book, enhancing your reading and writing skills every step of the way.

Teacher's notes

Introduction

The *Beat Dyslexia* series of books has been designed to help any child, teenager or adult who is struggling to read, write or spell. The books may be used by parents, teachers or tutors working on a one-to-one basis or with small groups. Books 1 to 3 work on the basics, introducing all the consonants, blends (e.g. pr, pl) and digraphs (two letters representing one sound: ng, th, sh, ch) and the short vowels. High-frequency words, the alphabet, basic punctuation and grammar (the verb, noun and adjective) are all taught using presentations that are clear and also interesting and entertaining. Books 4 and 5 in the series deal with long vowels and other spelling patterns, and provide literacy support through primary and early secondary-school level.

The main features of the programme include the following:

- A **carefully structured programme** that helps the learner understand the linguistic and phonological structures that underpin literacy. Pupils learn letter–sound relationships, how letters make words, the significance of vowels and consonants, how to recognise rhyme and syllables in words and how to recognise spelling patterns in the English language.

- A **conventional multi-sensory approach** that encourages the pupil to use most senses in order to learn letter–sound relationships. Looking and saying as well as hearing and writing reinforce learning through visual, auditory and kinaesthetic approaches. Wooden or plastic alphabet letters offer the chance to feel the shape of letters and to link this with speaking the sound, hearing the sound, looking at the shape of the letter and creating a neuro-muscular memory of the movement required to write the letter by hand. This approach is based on earlier work by Orton, Gillingham and Stillman and Hickey, who established the principles of multi-sensory teaching for dyslexic pupils.

- A **controlled vocabulary**, which means that in the early stages of the scheme learners are presented with reading passages made up from words which only contain letters and letter combinations they have already learned. There is also a steady introduction to the high-frequency words of the English language.

- The **Reading and Spelling Pack** and the **wooden alphabet** are an integral part of the programme. Their regular use in the earlier books offers reinforcement learning of the basics of sound–letter relationships as well as practice in the sequencing of the alphabet.

- The **CD** provides the auditory input of the programme, with exercises on sound recognition in words, short-term memory training, dictation and listening comprehension.

How to use *Beat Dyslexia*

Before you begin make sure you have the following equipment:

Set of wooden or plastic alphabet letters (upper case) for spelling practice.

Sharp pencil (a pencil grip may be helpful)

Lined exercise book

CD player (and CD provided with this book)

Reading/Spelling Pack cards provided with this book

Set of crayons or felt-tip pens

Timer or stop watch

Scissors

- *Beat Dyslexia* has been carefully designed and structured so that learning is cumulative, and also fun. It is therefore essential to follow the order of the pages and the order of the exercises on the pages. Do not skip pages or sections.

- Try to teach on a regular and frequent basis so that there is reinforcement learning of teaching points.

- Encourage your pupil to practise the Reading **and** Spelling Pack as often as possible. This versatile card pack can be used in two ways:

  1 To drill knowledge of individual letter–sound relationships (as described overleaf).

  2 To develop an understanding of how letters can be assembled to make words. The exercises in this book will help you get the idea. You will then be able to combine the cards collected from all the books to give practice in word building that is appropriate to the individual needs of your pupil.

  e.g.

- You can work at the pace that suits your pupil. Try to ensure that each teaching point has been successfully learned before progressing to the next. There are spelling tests and reading passages throughout the books, which will help you gauge your pupil's progress. Remember that praise and encouragement are the keys to successful learning. Ensure all goals are achievable and provide the right challenge for the pupil.

- Additional copies of the audio CD and packs of the Reading and Spelling Cards are available. Please contact the LDA Customer Services Team on 0845 120 4776.

A *Beat Dyslexia* lesson

Many of the lessons in this workbook are designed to introduce and then reinforce a letter or letter pattern. These lessons always follow the same format and most of the instructions are on the worksheet. The notes below will help you follow the methods shown on those pages and other pages.

Introduction

The letter pattern is introduced with a clueword picture and phrase.

Handwriting

Accurate formation of letters should be established from the beginning, so that handwriting is integral to the learning process – kinaesthetic link.

Listening activity

The pupil may listen to the audio CD or the teacher may read the script on pages x–xiv.

Identification

The letter pattern is underlined or highlighted in a string of letters or word search.

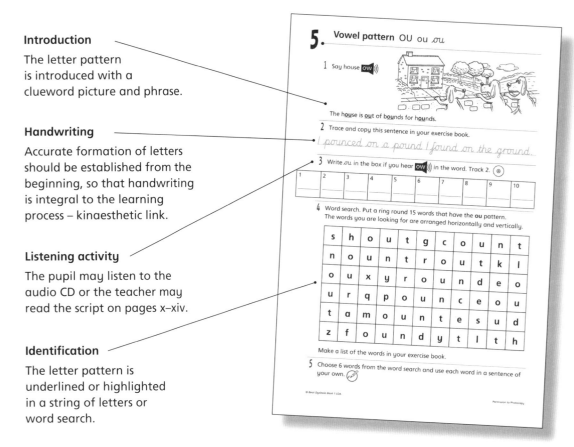

Writing activity

The pupil writes from dictation or creates sentences using the new letter pattern.

Reading

A short passage gives practice in reading the new letter pattern.

Reading and Spelling Cards

This icon means that the pupil should practise using the card sets.

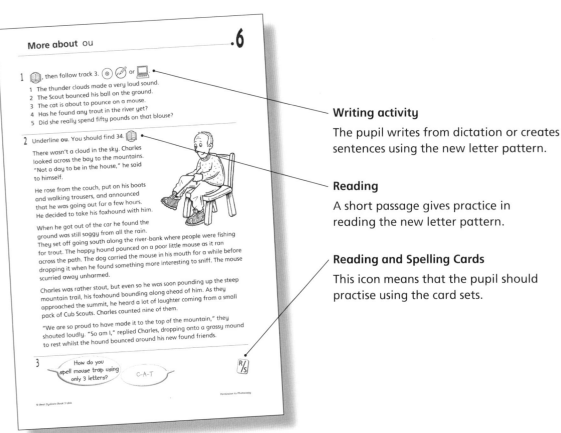

Multi-sensory introduction of the new letter pattern

The pupil says the clueword with the teacher in order to establish the speech sound which goes with the letter pattern. The pupil also traces and copies the handwritten letter form and completes a listening task. The teacher may choose to use the wooden alphabet letters so the pupil can feel the sequence of shapes in a newly introduced letter pattern. The pupil may then spell and read words made from the wooden letters.

Reading and Spelling Pack

The Reading and Spelling Pack is a key component in the *Beat Dyslexia* programme and should be practised daily. The purpose of the pack is to provide the pupils with practice in looking at and saying letters as well as hearing and writing them.

To practise looking and saying, the pupil should follow this procedure:

1 Look at the letter on the front of the card, and then remember and say the clueword and the sound.

2 Turn the card over to check that the word and sound are correct. If the pupil got it right, they place the card on the table, picture side up. If wrong, the card goes to the bottom of the pack, letter side up, so they can have another try.

3 Proceed to the next card.

To practise hearing and writing the pupil should do the following:

1 Listen as the teacher says the letter-sound. The pupil then repeats the sound and adds its alphabetical letter name.

e.g. **ow**))) ou

2 They should then write the letter or letter pattern in their exercise book using joined-up handwriting as taught and using the example on the card to compare with their effort. The logo reminds the pupil to add the new card to their pack when work on that particular letter-sound has been completed. It is also a reminder to practise the pack, drilling only the letters the pupil has covered so far. This way the pupil acquires confidence in their understanding of the principles underlying literacy skill as knowledge is consolidated in the growing Reading and Spelling Pack.

Handwriting

Use the guidelines provided on the page. You will see that every letter starts on the line. This simple rule is an essential part of learning for the dyslexic or dyspraxic pupil or the pupil with visuo-motor or visuo-perceptual difficulties. In order to achieve the desired result, the teacher must ensure that the pupil always starts on the line, with the entry stroke, and finishes with the exit stroke.

Listening activity ⊙

Use this reference section if you are not using the accompanying instruction CD and wish to read the words to your student or pupil. The exercises are either listening or dictation exercises. Read steadily and clearly. Make sure the pupil uses joined-up handwriting when writing in the box, on the page or in the exercise book.

Page 2 Section 7: DICTATION. Listen carefully and write this passage in your exercise book or on the computer.
    1 Can you remember your way home?
    2 You must drive your car over the bridge and back to the city centre.
    3 Take a left turn at the corner of North Street.
    4 Try to keep off the kerb.
    5 Use your map at this stage.
    6 Look for Pool Road.
    7 The rooms where you are staying are at number twenty.   [Track 1]

Page 5 Section 3: Write *ou* in the box if you hear the sound **ow**))) in the word.
    1 shout 2 hoop 3 hound 4 flounce 5 south 6 bone 7 bounce 8 space
    9 sprout 10 fountain   [Track 2]

Page 6 Section 1: DICTATION. Listen carefully and write the sentences in your exercise book or on the computer.
    1 The thunder clouds made a very loud sound.
    2 The Scout bounced his ball on the ground.
    3 The cat is about to pounce on a mouse.
    4 Has he found any trout in the river yet?
    5 Did she really spend fifty pounds on that blouse?   [Track 3]

Page 13 Section 2: Write the word you hear in the correct column on the page. Remember that a 1-syllable word ends **ck**))), spelled -ick, and a word of 2 or more syllables ends **ik**))), spelled -ic.
    1 flick 2 public 3 stick 4 chick 5 music 6 kick 7 elastic 8 topic 9 trick
    10 fantastic   [Track 4]

Page 18 Section 1: Write *tion* in the box if you hear **sh'n**))) at the end of the word.
    1 parachute 2 hallucination 3 machine 4 concentration 5 information
    6 essential 7 reaction 8 delicious 9 fascination 10 vindication   [Track 5]

Page 18 Section 3: DICTATION. Listen carefully and write the sentences in your exercise book or on the computer.
    1 I met my friend at the station.
    2 He did not mention that the jug was empty.
    3 The United Kingdom is a nation.
    4 I must give my work my full attention.
    5 We went to the meeting and asked many questions.
    6 He needs to pass the examination.   [Track 6]

Page 22 Section 2: Write the word in the correct column on the page.
    1 trifle 2 kettle 3 Bible 4 middle 5 little 6 steeple 7 battle 8 able   [Track 7]

Page 22 Section 5: DICTATION. Listen carefully and write the sentences in your exercise book or on the computer.
    1 The ducks waddle and paddle in the puddle.
    2 The cattle stumble and trample on the long wet grass.
    3 The horses were startled by the crackle of gunfire.   [Track 8]

Page 26 Section 1: DICTATION Listen carefully and write the words and then the sentences in your exercise book or on the computer.

    1 crutch 2 ditch 3 snatch 4 stretch

    1 Dad made a sketch of Patch the dog.

    2 A witch can make you itch and scratch if she puts a spell on you.

    3 The children play catch and hopscotch in the park.   [Track 9]

Page 27 Section 4: Repeat this shopping list after me. The list gets longer and longer as I think of more things to buy.

    milk milk and bread milk, bread and potatoes milk, bread, potatoes and butter milk, bread, potatoes, butter and soup milk, bread, potatoes, butter, soup and cheese milk, bread, potatoes, butter, soup, cheese and apples milk, bread, potatoes, butter, soup, cheese, apples and jam milk, bread, potatoes, butter, soup, cheese, apples, jam and fish   [Track 10]

Page 29 Section 4: Write *ir* in the box if you hear the sound er))) in the word.

    1 shirt 2 quirk 3 alarm 4 storm 5 mirth 6 path 7 swirl 8 kirk 9 meek 10 stir   [Track 11]

Page 30 Section 1: Write the number of the word you hear in the box, next to the word, on the page.

    1 shirt 2 thirsty 3 swerve 4 term 5 circulation 6 stir 7 skirt 8 first 9 verse

    10 thirst 11 third 12 circle 13 thermal 14 herd   [Track 12]

Page 30 Section 2: DICTATION Listen carefully and write the words and then the sentences in your exercise book or on the computer.

    1 girl 2 first 3 circle 4 skirt 5 squirm 6 circus

    1 There are thirteen dirty socks, skirts, shirts, vests and pairs of pants in the wash.

    2 There is a small, pretty, brown bird chirping in the fir tree.

    3 She will be thirty next birthday.   [Track 13]

Page 33 Section 4: Write *ur* in the box if you hear the sound er))) in the word.

    1 burning 2 surfers 3 garden 4 storing 5 urgent 6 curly 7 Spartan 8 unfurling

    9 foaming 10 turf   [Track 14]

Page 34 Section 3: DICTATION Listen carefully and write the words and then the sentences in your exercise book or on the computer.

    1 turn 2 burning 3 disturb 4 curve 5 urgently 6 church

    1 He will return by Thursday.

    2 The purple balloon burst when he sat on it.

    3 The nurse dropped his purse.   [Track 15]

Page 37 Section 3: Write *oy* in the box if you hear oy))) at the end of the word.

    1 coy 2 toy 3 spray 4 Troy 5 crow 6 convoy 7 alloy 8 how 9 destroy 10 joy [Track 16]

Page 38 Section 3: Listen to the individual sounds you hear and put a ring round the word you think they make.

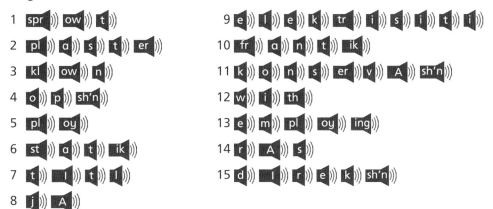

    [Track 17]

Page 41 Section 3: Write _oi_ in the box if you hear [oy]))) in the word.
    1 toil 2 choice 3 place 4 avoid 5 house 6 poison 7 exploit 8 join 9 horse
    10 noise   [Track 18]

Page 42 Section 2: DICTATION Listen carefully and write the words and then the sentences in your exercise book or on the computer.
    1 annoy 2 oil 3 employ 4 soil 5 royal 6 joint
    1 "What noise annoys an oyster?" asked the boy.
    2 "A noisy noise annoys an oyster," replied Roy.
    3 "Never put boiling oil into a plastic bottle," said Joyce in a loud voice.   [Track 19]

Page 49 Section 5: Write the words in the correct column on the page.
    1 shy 2 high 3 tie 4 tries 5 my 6 sigh 7 thigh 8 pie 9 try   [Track 20]

Page 53 Section 2: Write _au_ in the box if you hear the [aw]))) sound in the word.
    1 cause 2 lunch 3 launch 4 August 5 ounce 6 howl 7 haul 8 taunt 9 pause
    10 joint   [Track 21]

Page 54 Section 1: Underline or highlight the word you hear on the page.
    1 sauce 2 flaunt 3 launder 4 automatic 5 haunt   [Track 22]

Page 54 Section 2: Write headings _ou_ and _au_ in your exercise book or on the computer. Now write these words in the correct column.
    1 proud 2 pause 3 pouch 4 paunch 5 hound 6 mouse 7 gaunt 8 bouncing
    9 caution 10 automatic   [Track 23]

Page 56 Section 1: Complete the pictures by following these instructions.
    1 Draw a moon above the house.
    2 Draw a man walking across the bridge.
    3 Draw a cat running after the mouse.
    4 Draw a man peeping out from behind the door.
    5 Draw a tree between the lamp posts.
    6 Draw a woman under the umbrella.
    7 Draw a burglar breaking into the house.
    8 Draw a girl walking towards the school gates.
    9 Draw a pupil sitting at his desk.
    10 Draw a vase of flowers on the table.   [Track 24]

Page 56 Section 3: Listen and write the correct preposition under each picture.
    1 The train is going through the tunnel.
    2 The milk is in the fridge.
    3 The cat is under the table.
    4 The boy is holding hands with his girlfriend.
    5 The sandy seabed is beneath the shipwreck.
    6 The man is behind the shower curtain.
    7 The plane is on the runway.
    8 The sweets are from the sweet tin.
    9 The light is over the table.
    10 The dog is near the edge of the pool.   [Track 25]

Page 57 Section 2: Tick the word you hear on the page.
    1 cow 2 saw 3 drawn 4 raw 5 owning 6 bawl 7 down 8 awe 9 low 10 brawn
                                                                [Track 26]

Page 58 Section 1: DICTATION Listen carefully and write these sentences in your exercise book or on the computer.
    1 Raw prawns should be boiled before eating.

2 The tawny owl swooped swiftly and caught the mouse with its claws.

3 He scrawled his name on the picture he had drawn.   [Track 27]

Page 58 Section 2: Write these nouns and adjectives under the correct heading in your exercise book or on the computer.

1 energy 2 noisy 3 curl 4 noise 5 energetic 6 curly 7 anger 8 angry   [Track 28]

Page 58 Section 3: Listen and complete these sentences by writing the word in the space on the page

1 He insists he saw a flying saucer last Thursday night.

2 The Japanese love raw squid dipped in horse-radish sauce.

3 No one knows what caused dinosaurs to become extinct.

4 The exhaust coming from Paul's car is against the law.

5 The author attended the launch of his latest book and agreed to sign copies of the first edition for the audience.

6 I love paw-paw but I have never tasted mango or strawberries.

7 The children caught the trout when fishing in the river.

8 Jaundice is a disease of the liver and causes yellowing of the skin.

9 Laura went to audition for a part in the pantomime.

10 A lovely brown shawl covered her scrawny shoulders.   [Track 29]

Page 61 Section 4: Write these words under the correct headings in your exercise book or on the computer.

1 phantom 2 cough 3 cuff 4 farm 5 sniff 6 enough 7 fail 8 graph 9 fetch
10 gruff 11 laugh 12 physics   [Track 30]

Page 65 Section 4: DICTATION Listen carefully and write these words and sentences in your exercise book or on the computer.

1 curfew 2 drew 3 yew 4 Hebrew 5 jewel 6 chew

1 The curlew flew over the grassy dale.

2 My nephew pointed to the view.

3 There were a few pewter mugs for sale.

4 The crew pulled down the sails as the gale grew stronger and blew hard.   [Track 31]

Page 67 Section 3: Write the number of the word in the box on the page.

1 Rain. Heavy rain stopped play.   2 Wait. They had to wait for a taxi.   3 There. There will be seventy people at the party.   4 Slay. St George had to slay the dragon.   5 Eight. He got up at eight o'clock.   6 Reign. We are living in the reign of Queen Elizabeth II.   7 Ate. He ate a huge ice cream.   8 Weight. He is too heavy and is going to have to lose weight.   9 Vain. That woman is very vain about her appearance.   10 Veil. The bride wore a veil attached to a diamond tiara.
11 Their. Their home is in Washington DC.   12 Vane. The weather vane indicates a wind from the west today.   13 Vein. They mined a deep vein of coal.   14 Way. He lost his way in Nottingham after leaving the M1.   15 Vale. The Vale of Evesham is well known for its fruit and vegetable produce.   16 Sleigh. Sleigh bells are ringing tonight.   17 Reins. He held onto the reins of the horse.   18 Weigh. How much does that bag of potatoes weigh?   [Track 32]

Page 69 Section 4: Listen and write the number of each word in the box on the page.

1 hue 2 June 3 drew 4 tube 5 duke 6 true 7 Jew 8 rule 9 flute 10 chew
11 yew 12 mule 13 flew 14 argue 15 blue 16 clue 17 due 18 skew   [Track 33]

Page 70 Section 1: DICTATION Listen carefully and write these words and sentences in your exercise book or on the computer.

1 rescue 2 value 3 argue 4 continue 5 clue 6 blue

1 I haven't a clue if that is true.

2 They painted the statue blue.

3 Why argue about the value of the Queen's jewels?   [Track 34]

Page 71 Section 1: Listen to the long-vowel sounds in these words. Write the word in the correct box on the page.

1 tune   2 light   3 stole   4 fake   5 rail   6 weep   7 wipe   8 cube   9 team   10 thief   11 flow
12 loaf   13 stay   14 spy   15 drew   16 blue   17 display   18 reply   19 inhale   20 ignite
21 mainly   22 clue   23 invoke   24 blowing   25 indeed   26 approach   27 reason   28 brighter
29 nephew   30 believe   31 costume   32 waiter   33 between   34 value   35 diesel   36 supply
37 safely   38 runway   39 screamed   40 fighting   41 pillow   42 toasted   43 curfew
44 define   45 encode   [Track 35]

Page 73 Section 2: Number these words in the brackets after each word, on the page.
1 jealous   2 adventurous   3 marvellous   4 famous   5 generous   6 tremendous
7 poisonous   8 treacherous   9 venomous   10 ridiculous   [Track 36]

Page 77 Section 4: Listen to this passage on bird migration and note the key points. Use your notes to answer the questions.

Migration in birds has been studied closely. For example, swallows nest in Britain and Europe during the summer. Then, as winter approaches and the young are strong enough to fly, the swallows gather together in flocks, preparing to make their incredible journey south to Africa, where they remain until the following spring. When they return to Europe the round trip can be as much as 19,000 kilometres. Amazingly they sometimes return to the same nests. Experts think that they are guided by the sun during the day and by the stars at night. Of course, a few birds get blown off course by storms and lose their way. Other summer visitors to Britain include cuckoos, nightingales and warblers.

Scientists catch birds and place marked rings around their legs. Birds which are found later can yield information to scientists about how far they have travelled and the routes they have taken. One seabird, which was released in America, flew back 4,800 kilometres to its nest on an island off the Welsh coast. The longest distance covered by a migrating bird in a single journey is 17,600 kilometres. This record is held by the Arctic tern, which travels south from the Arctic to winter in the Antarctic.

Questions:
1 Name a bird which migrates.   2 When do swallows nest in Europe?   3 Where do swallows migrate to in winter?   4 Do swallows ever return to the same nests?   5 Name one other summer visitor to Britain.   6 What is the longest distance covered by a migrating bird?   7 How are migrating birds guided by day?   8 How are migrating birds guided by night?   9 What can cause a migrating bird to lose its way?   10 How do scientists track migrating birds?   [Track 37]

Page 81 Section 4: Write the headings for the three sounds for the letters ch in your exercise book or on the computer. Write the words you hear in the correct column.
1 Christmas   2 machine   3 chocolate   4 charging   5 technical   6 chalet   7 chosen
8 brochure   9 school   10 challenge   11 parachute   12 stomach   [Track 38]

Spelling tests Sp

At intervals throughout the book, a logo tells the user to ask the teacher for a spelling test. Read the words carefully and clearly. Be sure to include the words in brackets if there is ambiguity about the spelling. The words could be given as homework, preparatory to testing.

Page 2 Section 2:
1 being   2 thought   3 goes   4 heard (I heard him say that.)   5 could   6 any   7 during
8 young   9 only   10 before   11 every   12 half   13 change   14 friend   15 leave   16 year
17 told   18 both   19 above   20 always

Page 20 Section 5:
   1 cloud   2 safely   3 plastic   4 our (belonging to us)   5 laugh   6 question   7 shout   8 earth
   9 magic   10 station   11 decide   12 usually   13 mountain   14 important   15 objection
   16 water   17 electric   18 length   19 ground   20 suddenly

Page 31 Section 4:
   1 people   2 matches   3 armies   4 first   5 separate   6 turnip   7 where (question word)
   8 witches   9 disturb   10 sure (I am sure of that fact.)   11 little   12 different   13 watch
   14 work   15 wives   16 impossible   17 turtle   18 through (He walked through the door.)
   19 shirt   20 money

Page 36 Section 3: Use the Reading/Spelling cards as indicated on the page.
   1 emu   2 idle   3 motion   4 music   5 mount   6 turn   7 first   8 rifle   9 station   10 foundation

Page 52 Section 5:
   1 employ   2 coin   3 angrily   4 although   5 field   6 untie   7 following   8 believe   9 family
   10 loyal   11 quietly   12 relief   13 definite   14 joint   15 original   16 quickly   17 cries
   18 poisoned   19 although   20 planned

Page 70 Section 4:
   1 launch   2 you're (I'm sure you're right.)   3 prawn   4 alphabet   5 except   6 few
   7 weight (How heavy?)   8 glue   9 automatic   10 minute   11 suitable   12 they've
   13 crawling   14 dolphin   15 science   16 naturally   17 chew   18 eight (number)
   19 continue   20 caught (I caught the ball.)

Page 88 Section 4:
   1 actually   2 chemist   3 receive   4 fabulous   5 pointing   6 certain   7 centre   8 enormous
   9 hospital   10 million   11 special   12 bodies   13 nervous   14 method   15 machine
   16 escaping   17 effortless   18 gently   19 realistic   20 probably

Other lessons

Essential spellings

These pages teach spelling of high-frequency words with the emphasis on joined-up handwriting as an aid to memory.

Reading passages

These are provided at regular intervals and comprise short passages and stories that are structured to include the letter patterns that are being taught. The student's ability to decode is fostered by the fact that they are only asked to read passages that are made up from letters, words and high-frequency words that they have already learned. Thus self-esteem, willingness and a confident ability to decode are generated. All the passages are photocopiable. For pupils with Scotopic Sensitivity Syndrome photocopying onto coloured paper is often helpful.

Long-vowel choices chart

The long-vowel choices chart provides a systematic way for the pupil to build up a list of the spelling choices for each long-vowel sound. Spelling patterns are recorded according to their position in words. For example, 'ee' can be in the main part of the word as in 'queen', or at the end of a word, as in 'bee'. Most helpfully, the long-vowel choices chart indicates the frequency of occurrence of a long-vowel spelling pattern by listing it as 1st try, 2nd try, and so on. This helps the pupil to make a reasonable guess at a long-vowel spelling.

Sorting cards

Not included in this book, but recommended as a helpful method for reading practice at this stage, is the making of a pack of forty cards. Select ten words that are to be reinforced. Write these out four times and make cards. The cards may be used for traditional games such as Snap, Rummy, Pelmanism (Pairs) and Happy Families, or simply for sorting.

Reading Games

Family Fours (page 71)

This game is played with a minimum of three players and a set of cards. After completing the spelling task on page 71, carefully cut out the forty-five words and stick each at the top of a small, blank playing card. Cards are then placed face down in the middle of the table and players take it in turn to pick up and read a card. The first player picks up a card, reads it and then places it face upwards in front of themselves, as the first player. As the next player picks up and reads a card, that player looks to see if there are any cards with the same family letter pattern in front of any other players. If there are, then that player can claim them. In this way a complete family of four cards is built up and the winner is the player who collects most families.

Bingo

The teacher writes a list of at least fifteen words on the board or on a sheet of paper. Each player chooses five or six words from the list and writes them down. The teacher then reads out from the list on the board, at random. Players cross off the words on their own lists as they are read out. The first to cross off all their words shouts 'Bingo'.

Notes on page 48: Conjunctions

The revised passage is as follows:

I once spent a wonderful day beside a rushing river in the north of Scotland. We picnicked on the short grass **and** we passed the time relaxing in the sunshine. We chose a spot near a waterfall **because** we wanted to watch the salmon leaping. The signal that it was time for some action came **when** we noticed a crowd starting to gather on the platform overhanging the waterfall. The water was crystal clear **so** we could observe the amazing creatures swimming purposefully upstream over the pebbles. Suddenly we would see a flash of wriggling silver as a brave female flung herself up over the rapids. **Although** she dashed herself on the rocks as she fought the current, this did not deter her. Often she would be washed back down to start again. She would land just short of the pool above. It might take several attempts, **but** usually she would succeed. We hoped she would reach her spawning ground to lay her eggs.

Notes on page 83: Proofreading

To proofread for spelling errors successfully, teach the pupil to work from the end to the beginning, reading one word at a time. This mitigates against the pupil reading what they think appears. The corrected passage is as follows:

After breakfast we packed our bags and went to our next destination, which was two miles away. Our Cub leader said it would take us one hour to get there, but we thought it would take longer and we set off. It did only take us one hour.

When we reached our destination, we pitched our tents quickly so we had time to go for a walk, which we did not like, but we made a deal that if we went for a walk, we could have a camp fire that night. The walk was not too long and we got our badges for walking two miles, and at least we had someone to talk to. It was nearly two o'clock so we had some lunch. We did some archery and athletics, closely supervised, until five o'clock.

We had a bit of a shock at five o'clock because a sponsored walk came right through where our tents were pitched, so we had to move our tents. By the time we had moved our tents, it was getting dark and we had our camp fire and the Cub leader had some marshmallows. We cooked them on the bonfire. Then we had a game of football in the dark. We pretended to go to sleep.

When the Cub leader had gone, we sneaked out and got up to some mischief. We got back into our tents an hour or so later. Then we just talked for the rest of the night.

This piece of writing offers an opportunity for a good discussion, raising the following points:

1   On the positive side, this is a good piece of writing which gives an interesting picture of life at the Cub camp.
2   However, the sentences are too long in some parts. How could these be split up?
3   The writer needs to be taught the difference between 'our' and 'are' and 'to', 'two' and 'too'.
4   There are no paragraphs.
5   The concept of the past tense ending 'ed' needs to be taught.

Guide to logos used in *Beat Dyslexia 5*

E)))	Sound (includes appropriate letter)
R/S	Add new card to your pack and practise the cards you have collected so far
CD	Listen to CD
Read	Read
Write	Write
CD + Write	Listen to CD and write. The task will usually be a dictation. You will find the appropriate track on the accompanying CD. Instead you may use the CD transcript in these notes to read to your pupil.
A E I O U	Fill in the long-vowel pattern you have learned on the long-vowel choices chart
Sp	Ask your teacher to read the spelling test words
computer	Use the word processor (computer) as an alternative to handwriting

a　b　c　d

e　f　g　h　i

j　k　l　m　n

o　p　q　r

s　t　u　v

w　x　y　z

Long-vowel choices chart

Long-vowel sound picture	Open syllable	Main part of word					End of word		
		1st try	2nd try	3rd try	4th try	5th try	1st try	2nd try	3rd try
A	a|corn	a-e	ai	ei			ay	y	
E	e|quals	ee	ea	e-e	ie	ei	ee	ea	e-e
I	i|ron	i-e	igh				y	igh	ie
O	o|pen	o-e	oa	ow			ow		
U	u|nit	u-e	ew				ew	ue	

1. Check your skills

You will need a pencil, exercise book and dictionary.

1 Say the alphabet to your teacher, **naming** each letter. Which letters are the vowels? Copy these words into your exercise book and underline the vowel or vowels in each case.

strong   sheep   train   packed   judge

2 Write the alphabet in sequence in your exercise book using lower-case letters, and then tell your teacher the **sound** of each letter.

3 What is a dictionary? Can you use a dictionary?
How quickly can you find these words?

dodge   hexagon   pelican   scribe

4 Are you using joined-up handwriting?
Write your name in joined-up handwriting in your exercise book.

5 Point to the word which matches the correct definition.

_____ is always a 'doing' or 'being' word.
e.g. 'doing' words: **swim think speak**
　　　'being' words: **am were was**

A noun

_____ is a section of writing. It is made up of sentences which are all about the same subject matter. Writing is divided into these sections to help understanding.

A verb

_____ is a unit of meaning. It makes sense. In order to make complete sense it must have a verb. It must also start with a capital letter and finish with a full stop.

An adjective

_____ is a describing word. It tells you something about a noun (place, person or thing).
e.g. **large beautiful heavy pink**

A paragraph

_____ is always a naming word. It is the name of a person, place or thing, even things you can't touch.
e.g. **Robin Hood London zebra anger sleep life herd team**

A sentence

6 Now give your teacher an example of each of these:

noun   verb   adjective   sentence

Check your skills

1 Trace and copy this sentence in your exercise book twice, using joined-up writing. Refer to page xviii if you need help in forming the letters.

The quick brown fox jumps over the lazy dog.

2 (Sp) Can you spell some of the most frequently used words?
Listen to your teacher and write down the twenty spellings you hear in your exercise book. Listen carefully and use joined-up writing.

3 Say the days of the week in the right order. Can you spell them?

4 What is the Doubling rule? Can you spell these words using the Doubling rule? Write them in your exercise book.

stop + ing =   whip + ed =

rub + er =   shop + er =

jog + ing =   pack + ing =

fit + ed =   rest + ed =

5 Follow the rule for adding a vowel suffix to a word that ends in **e**.

like + ed =   dine + ing =

wave + y =   ride + er =

smile + ing =   bone + y =

rule + er =   brake + ed =

6 Say the months of the year in the right order.
Can you spell them?

7 Can you use capital letters, full stops and question marks correctly?
Listen to the short dictation passage on the CD and write it down
in your exercise book or on the computer. Pay attention to punctuation.
Track 1. (◎) or

3. Multiple-choice questions

Show your answer by ticking the box.
Score 1 point for each correct answer.

1 A syllable is:

   1 a beat in a word
   2 a pudding
   3 a group of words with meaning.

1
2
3

2 A consonant is:

   1 a word which joins two parts of a sentence
   2 a letter which is not a vowel
   3 a large land mass.

1
2
3

3 When a sentence begins with who/what/when/where/why, it should end with:

   1 an exclamation mark
   2 a comma
   3 a question mark.

1
2
3

4 Plural means:

   1 one only
   2 more than one
   3 changing **f** to **v** and adding **s**.

1
2
3

5 Complete this sentence with the right word:

She took _____ dogs for a walk.
   1 their
   2 there

1
2

6 The plural form of loaf is:

   1 loafs
   2 loavs
   3 loaves.

1
2
3

7 The plural form of cherry is:

   1 cherrys
   2 cherries
   3 cherris.

1
2
3

What is a sentence?

To improve sentence structure you must first understand what
a sentence is. A sentence is a group of words which make sense.
Speaking gives you an instinctive idea of a sentence because you
usually pause at the end of one.

1 Read these passages aloud to help you get a sense of what a sentence
is. As you begin to get the meaning you will find yourself pausing. Each
pause, at the end of a string of words which make sense, shows you have
reached the end of a sentence. Mark it with a full stop.

1 Living in London is so different from living at home it is very big
   with many streets shops and cars our apartment is quite cramped
   with very little space it has only three rooms but we manage I have
   already seen most of the sights like Tower Bridge and Big Ben I have
   also seen the Tower of London and the London Eye everyone at school
   is nice to me but it is hard not knowing much English

2 Flora was sure she had been here before something about the place
   was familiar the shop on the corner of the street reminded her of days
   gone by she had gone into that shop many times in the past something
   disturbing was awaking in her memory and she became fearful

2 Identifying sentences. Which of these are sentences and which are not?

   1 for ten minutes
   2 he played football for Manchester United
   3 under the bridge
   4 he fell down
   5 I like our new home
   6 by the river
   7 the car needed more petrol
   8 then it began to rain
   9 off the end of the runway
   10 as a clown

You should have identified 5 sentences. Look at them again and see that
they each have a verb – action/doing word. A sentence must have a **verb**.

5. Vowel pattern OU ou *ou*

1 Say house

The h**ou**se is **ou**t of b**ou**nds for h**ou**nds.

2 Trace and copy this sentence in your exercise book.

I pounced on a pound I found on the ground.

3 Write *ou* in the box if you hear **ow**))) in the word. Track 2. ◎

1	2	3	4	5	6	7	8	9	10

4 Word search. Put a ring round 15 words that have the **ou** pattern.
The words you are looking for are arranged horizontally and vertically.

s	h	o	u	t	g	c	o	u	n	t
n	o	u	n	t	r	o	u	t	k	l
o	u	x	y	r	o	u	n	d	e	o
u	r	q	p	o	u	n	c	e	o	u
t	a	m	o	u	n	t	e	s	u	d
z	f	o	u	n	d	y	t	l	t	h

Make a list of the words in your exercise book.

5 Choose 6 words from the word search and use each word in a sentence of your own. 🖊

1 , then follow track 3.   or

    1 The thunder clouds made a very loud sound.
    2 The Scout bounced his ball on the ground.
    3 The cat is about to pounce on a mouse.
    4 Has he found any trout in the river yet?
    5 Did she really spend fifty pounds on that blouse?

2 Underline **ou**. You should find 34.

There wasn't a cloud in the sky. Charles looked across the bay to the mountains. "Not a day to be in the house," he said to himself.

He rose from the couch, put on his boots and walking trousers, and announced that he was going out for a few hours. He decided to take his foxhound with him.

When he got out of the car he found the ground was still soggy from all the rain. They set off going south along the river-bank where people were fishing for trout. The happy hound pounced on a poor little mouse as it ran across the path. The dog carried the mouse in his mouth for a while before dropping it when he found something more interesting to sniff. The mouse scurried away unharmed.

Charles was rather stout, but even so he was soon pounding up the steep mountain trail, his foxhound bounding along ahead of him. As they approached the summit, he heard a lot of laughter coming from a small pack of Cub Scouts. Charles counted nine of them.

"We are so proud to have made it to the top of the mountain," they shouted loudly. "So am I," replied Charles, dropping onto a grassy mound to rest whilst the hound bounced around his new found friends.

3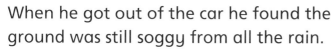

    How do you spell mouse trap using only 3 letters?

    C–A–T

7. Writing sentences and adding punctuation

1 Put these words into the right order to make sentences.
Write the sentences in your exercise book using correct punctuation.
Remember that a sentence always begins with a capital letter and ends
with a full stop.

1 the yesterday I hounds saw
2 going are we town to
3 falling trees the leaves are from
4 clean going is his to room he
5 driving are we school to
6 field that in horses are there
7 on summer hottest was it record the
8 like more eat to would I some
9 sailing they on lake are the
10 way the got she on lost the supermarket to

2 Read this passage and then write it out in 4 separate sentences, using a
capital letter at the start and a full stop at the end of each sentence.

the ginger cat streaked across the garden it stopped
suddenly a crow landed on the grass the cat sprang
but the crow flew off

3 Write 2 sentences about each of the following:

a dog

a trip to the seaside

going shopping

a car

Don't forget to use a capital letter and a full stop for each sentence.

1 A suffix is a letter or a group of letters which are added to the end of a word to change its meaning.

e.g. He slips.   Add suffixes: She jump_____ .

I am slipping.   I am jump_____ .

She slipped.   He jump_____ .

It is a slipper.   It is a jump_____ .

It is slippy.   She is jump_____ .

---

2 Suffix **-ful**. To use the word **full** as a suffix, drop one letter l.

e.g. hopeful, thankful, grateful, useful, careful

---

3 Add the following suffixes to complete this passage. Remember to use the rules for adding suffixes such as the Doubling rule and the rules for adding a suffix to a word which ends in **e** or **y**.

-s   -ing   -ly   -ed   -ment   -ful   -er

The parrot_____ were all mark_____ in bright shade_____

of green and red. They hop_____ about their cage_____

and chatter_____ and twitter_____ happy_____ . The

keep_____ was care_____ to feed them each day with

slice_____ of mango, melon and banana. They greet_____

her with excite_____ when they saw her come_____ .

Some of the more play_____ parrot_____ put on a show

for the visitor_____ who came to the park. They skilful_____

wheel_____ little carts up and down while other

parrot_____ jump_____ on and off. Parrot_____ are good

acrobat_____ . Everyone clap_____ loud_____ because the

parrots were so amuse_____ .

9. Our/are confusion

1 **Our** means 'belongs to us'. It answers the question 'Whose?'

e.g. **Whose** house? **Our** house.
Whose cat? **Our** cat.
Whose team? **Our** team.

Are is part of the verb 'to be'.
e.g. We **are** running. You **are** going. They **are** sleeping.

2 Fill in **our** or **are** to complete these sentences.

1 _____ car is large because we _____ a big family.

2 You _____ sleeping in _____ house tonight.

3 They _____ going to come and see _____ new computer.

4 We _____ happy to announce the arrival of _____ baby.

5 Samantha and Simon _____ friends.

6 There _____ no cracks in _____ walls.

7 _____ you coming to _____ party?

8 They _____ mending the roof of _____ garage.

3 Now write a sentence of your own using **are** and another using **our**.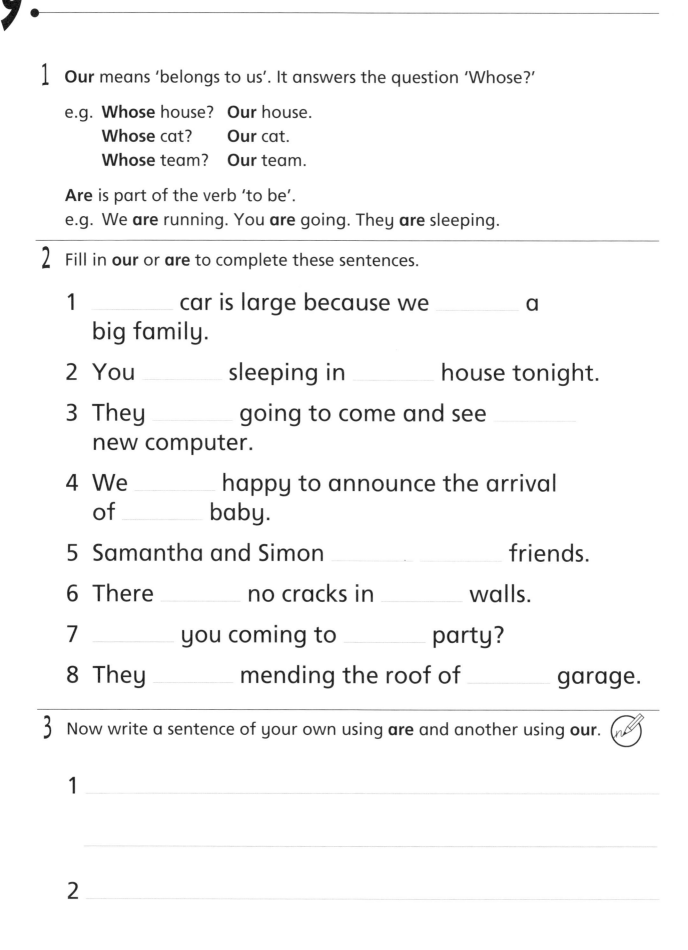

1 _____

_____

2 _____

_____

Punctuation practice: full stops and capital letters 10

1 Put a ring round every full stop, question mark and exclamation mark. Now 📖.

As Jack came into the room, he felt a cool breeze and went to close the back door. Had he left it open that morning? He didn't think so. A door banged on the landing and made him jump. He wished he had the dog with him and quickly picked up the cast-iron frying pan which he had left on top of the fridge. He stood stiffly, listening to the footsteps along the upper hallway, and tried hard not to

panic. Suddenly a shrill cry rang out in the stillness. It was his wife, but 'Is she alone?' he asked himself. He must save her at all costs, and squaring up to the task, he raced swiftly up to their room. As he spotted a huge, black shape hiding from him, behind the half-closed bedroom door, he tripped and fell flat, scared witless. He had fallen exactly at the feet of his large and lively wife, Prunella.

'April fool!' she yelled, smiling with amusement as he gazed up at her, pale and tired.

Did you notice that there is a pause at the end of every unit of meaning and that this is marked by a full stop, question mark or exclamation mark?

2 Write out the following passages, adding only full stops and capital letters. You should have 5 sentences in each when you have finished. 🖊

it is stupid to say that you don't like teachers they are people like you and me some of them are fun and some of them are not in this school most of them are nice and they try to help their pupils you're angry with teachers just now because you've been punished

my mother and father asked me if I would like to go with them to a big sheep farm on Sunday I said I would like to go very much and I set my alarm clock to wake me at 7 o'clock that day we started off on the car trip along the road to the farm my dog barked as we left he wanted to go too but he had to stay in the yard and guard the house while we were away

11. Syllable ending -IC -ic -ic

1 Say traffic 🔊 🔊. The pattern -ic is found at the end of the final syllable in words of 2 or more syllables.

Frant**ic** pan**ic** in the traff**ic**.

2 Trace and copy this sentence in your exercise book.

The critics were ecstatic about his music.

3 Colour the vowels red. How many vowels are there in each word? How many syllables or beats are there in each word?

	Vowels	Beats
FORENSIC		
GASTRIC		
GALACTIC		
ATTIC		
HECTIC		
BASIC		
METALLIC		
SPASMODIC		

Read the words. If you do not know the meaning of a word, find it in the dictionary or ask your teacher to explain.

4 Use a coloured pen to trace and add the syllable ending -ic. Then read the words. 📖

com___   mag___   Pacif___   allerg___

energet___   exot___   trag___   fantast___

More about syllable ending -ic

1 Trace and complete the word by writing -ic in the blanks. Answer the questions by ticking the box.

	YES	NO

1 Do you believe in *mag*____?

2 Do you know where the *Pacif*____ Ocean is?

3 Are you *allerg*____ to anything?

4 Is your kettle *electr*____?

5 Do you like *mus*____?

6 Do you think *organ*____ food is good for you?

7 Have you ever been across the *Atlant*____?

8 Is your pencil case made of *plast*____?

9 Does your house have an *att*____?

10 Are you *optimist*____ about Leeds United?

2 📖

Dominic was ecstatic. The newspaper had paid him a fantastic sum for his article on sailing in the tropics. He had written about the challenge of crossing the Atlantic and about the magic of sailing in the Pacific. He had described his white plastic boat, which was far from basic. It had many up-to-date, electrical gadgets, including a computer which had helped him navigate the seas of the globe. This energetic, if eccentric, person was now optimistic about his career, writing about exotic places. He was planning another article on the topic of the music of Africa.

3 Write these words in sentences of your own. ✎

comic   tragic   hectic   pathetic   music   electric

13. Syllable ending -ic and 1-beat words ending in -ick

1 When you hear the [i] [k] sounds at the end of a 1-syllable (beat) word you must write -ick.

   📖 pick   trick   stick

   When you hear the [i] [k] sounds at the end of a 2-, 3- or 4-syllable word you must write -ic.

   📖 topic   Atlantic   diplomatic

2 Write the words you hear on the CD in the correct column. Track 4. 💿 ✏️

1 syllable	2 or more syllables
e.g. *brick*	*plastic*

3 📖 Use these words to fill the gaps in the sentences below.

   supersonic   optimistic   organic
   septic   fanatic   electric

   1 To think the best will happen is to be _____.
   2 A person obsessed by something is a _____.
   3 Some planes can travel at _____ speed.
   4 An _____ current can make steel magnetic.
   5 A cut which is infected is _____.
   6 _____ farming uses animal manure in place of synthetic fertilisers.

4 *What did Stone Age men like listening to?*   *Rock music*

R/S

Choosing words to make interesting sentences

1 Find an alternative for the underlined words in these sentences.

Write the sentences in your exercise book or on the computer. or

Brain storm for alternative words and then select one.

We had a <u>nice</u> day.
Everyone was very <u>nice</u> to her.
It was a <u>nice</u> lunch.

> tasty
> pleasant   good
> exciting   pretty   kind
> delicious   lovely   super
> nice   helpful   brilliant
> fantastic

2 Our dog <u>ran</u> after the sheep.
Ali <u>ran</u> all the way to school.
The spider <u>ran</u> across the bathroom floor.

> ran

3 The holiday was <u>good</u>.
I had a <u>good</u> time.
The teachers were <u>good</u>.

> good

4 I want to <u>get</u> some boots.
Please <u>get</u> me an ice cream.
He will <u>get</u> a place in the team.

> buy
> fetch   find   get
> earn   be   given
> try on   give   select
> win borrow

5 "Sh! Mum is asleep," <u>said</u> Dad.
"Come over here," <u>said</u> the teacher.
"Stop!" <u>said</u> the guard.

> said

15. Essential spellings

1 Work across. ⟶

Read	Trace, naming letters	Write
1 laugh	laugh	
2 decide	decide	
3 usually	usually	
4 water	water	
5 safely	safely	
6 suddenly	suddenly	
7 together	together	
8 important	important	
9 earth	earth	
10 length	length	

Reading with a purpose: choosing a holiday

Read about 3 different holidays and choose one for each family.

Beach Adventure Club is the ideal summer camp for 11–15-year-olds. Friendly, expert staff will teach you all kinds of sports. They'll take care of you so there's no need for Mum or Dad to worry. You can go snorkelling, play tennis or try water skiing. Book now to be sure of your place.

Glen Inverness Hotel is a peaceful retreat in the Scottish Highlands. Relax in the superb comfort of this four-star hotel. All rooms are en suite and have TV. Dogs are welcome. Go hiking and see wild deer on the hills or seals swimming in the sea. Fishing and golf are close by. Come back to a log fire, well-stocked bar and fine food.

Campsite Family Fun has over 20 different sites to choose from, in France, Germany and England. Large tents offer every comfort and there's a shop, restaurant and swimming pool on every site. Indoor and outdoor activities for the kids are organised by selected personnel. Half-price deals for kids mean this could be the holiday for you and your family. All from as little as £80 per week.

Frank is a retired teacher, married to Jean. They live in Manchester. Frank does not like to travel far any more because he is hard of hearing. He prefers holidays in Scotland or Wales. He likes to go fishing, while Jean is a keen golfer. They like to take their dog, Bruno, with them. Frank and Jean chose:

12-year-old James has just gone to live in Neasdon. He had to leave his friends in Melrose. His dad has to work hard at his new job in computer software and cannot take time off for a summer holiday. James has been unhappy since his parents split up and he needs to have fun with children of the same age. James and his dad chose:

Tracey and her partner Steve have three children: Mark 8, Wayne 6 and Jade 3. They have a limited budget and are looking for a holiday that keeps the kids happy so they can relax themselves. They haven't had a holiday for two years. Steve spent some time in Germany when he was young. Steve and Tracey chose:

17. Syllable pattern -TION -tion -*tion*

Found only at the end of words.

1 Say fraction **sh'n**))).

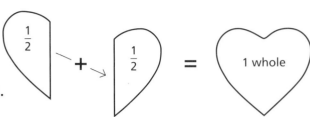

Attrac**tion** between frac**tion**s.

2 Trace and copy this sentence in your exercise book.

His destination is Paddington Station.

3 Split and count. How many syllables are there in these words?
Remember that **-tion** is 1 syllable and count the other vowels.

e.g.   Number of syllables

frac|tion   _____2_____
sub|trac|tion   _____3_____
inspection   _____
education   _____
objection   _____
population   _____
organisation   _____
relationship   _____
multiplication   _____
protection   _____

4 Words with **-tion** are nouns. They often come from verbs.
Add **-tion** to each verb.

verb ⟶ noun		verb ⟶ noun	
e.g. to explor**e**	an explora*tion*	to produce	a produc*tion*
to combin**e**	a combina_____	to collect	a collec_____
to invite	an _____	to invent	an _____
to prepare	a _____	to inject	an _____

Did you notice that **an** comes before a noun that starts with a vowel?

5 Now use your dictionary to find the definitions of these words.

evaporation   revolution   nation
condensation   probation   indigestion

More about -tion

1 Listen to the words on the CD and write *tion* in the box if you hear
sh'n))) at the end of a word. Track 5. (⊚)

1	2	3	4	5	6	7	8	9	10

2 Trace the handwritten word and complete it by adding *tion* or *tions*.

Punctua_____ was discussed in prepara_____ for the examina_____.

The teacher did some examples of correc_____. He then held a

conversa_____ with the students about the repeti_____ of mistakes.

He insisted that they take ac_____ about the situa_____. He told them

that a good educa_____ was a prepara_____ for life and that there

could be no separa_____ between English written work for school

examina_____ and what was needed for an adult working life.

Now 📖.

3 📖, then listen to track 6. (⊚) (✎) or 💻

  1 I met my friend at the station.
  2 He did not mention that the jug was empty.
  3 The United Kingdom is a nation.
  4 I must give my work my full attention.
  5 We went to the meeting and asked many questions.
  6 He needs to pass the examination.

4 Read and discuss the meaning of these proverbs with your teacher.

Necessity is the mother of invention.

Imitation is the sincerest form of flattery.

5

19. Crossword fun -TION

1 Choose from these words to complete the crossword.

ration	navigation	option	direction	attention
nation	adoration	caption	imagination	digestion
solution	subtraction	exhibition	action	function
adoption	question	junction	position	station

Across

1 The legal act of taking a child into one's family: a_____

3 Trains arrive or depart from one: s_____

6 A display of pictures or sculptures: e_____

8 A small portion of food allocated from a limited supply: r_____

12 A crossroad is a j_____

13 A population sharing the same land and government is a n_____

14 Instruction on how to get somewhere or do something: d_____

16 A picture in the mind: i_____

17 The answer to a problem is the s_____

18 Means by which a ship finds its destination: n_____

19 Words beneath a picture or cartoon: c_____

Down

1 Worship: a_____

2 An exact location: p_____

3 Minus or take away sum: s_____

4 Pay a_____

5 Ask a q_____

7 Process of breaking down food in the intestine: d_____

9 A movement of the body is an a_____

10 To choose means you have an o_____

11 To have a use: f_____

15 She sprang into a_____

Adjectives

1 List the adjectives in this passage. You should find 14.

He was a kind, funny and energetic person when he was a young man. Then he had the misfortune to lose his job and was in a serious accident which left him with a bad limp. For a while he turned into a mean and sulky person with a cruel tongue and a violent temper. Nothing amused him any more. Thankfully he got through this dark period of his life and became the wise, cheerful and generous person we are proud to call our friend.

2 Can you find the adjectives that mean the same as these words?
Use your dictionary. Write them in your exercise book.
Try to find at least 3 for each word.

e.g. 1 dirty – dusty, unwashed, unkempt, spattered, muddy, soiled, unclean, unpleasant, rough

2 big
3 small
4 nice

3 Adjectives help a sentence to make sense. Add adjectives to these sentences. Write the improved sentences in your exercise book.

1 She got feet when she stepped in a puddle.
2 My dad has hair, a nose and eyes.
3 Our dog has gone missing. It has a coat, ears and a tail.
4 I am hoping to buy a house with bedrooms and a kitchen.

4 Use interesting adjectives to describe the nouns in these sentences.

1 The _____ cat crept into the _____ house.
2 The _____ boy was eating a _____ pie.
3 The _____ girl sat on a _____ chair.
4 The _____ man was reading a _____ book.
5 The _____ teacher was talking to the _____ boy.
6 His _____ sweater was lying on the _____ floor.
7 The _____ dog lay in his _____ basket.
8 Our _____ neighbour is cleaning his _____ car.
9 The _____ trees are swaying in this _____ wind.

5 (Sp) Ask your teacher for a spelling test.

21. Consonant -le endings

-ble -dle -fle -gle -kle -ple -tle -zle

1 Baffled by the puzzle? Don't give up the struggle.

Fill in the consonant **-le** ending to complete the words.
Cut out the puzzle and mix up the pieces.
How quickly can you fit it together again?

-ble   bub___

-ple   ap___

-gle   wig___

-tle   bot___

-kle   pric___

-ble   ta___

-fle   tri___

-ple   stee___

---

2 Underline the **-le** endings.

A consonant after the vowel makes a closed syllable and a short-vowel sound.

e.g. rŭ|ffle| simple

meddle   chuckle

gentle   jungle

cattle   ankle

ripple   bundle

uncle   tremble

No consonant after the vowel makes an open syllable and a long-vowel sound.

e.g. tā|ble| poodle

title   cradle

feeble   noble

needle   cycle

rifle   bridle

people   gable

More about consonant -le endings

1 Copy twice in your exercise book. Tick the one you like the best.

He struggled to saddle his horse in the stable.

2 Listen to the words on CD track 7. ⊚ ✎ Write each word in the correct column.

Short vowel + 2 consonants before -le	Long vowel + 1 consonant before -le
e.g. *puzzle*	*cable*

3 Join the rhyming pairs. e.g. nibble ⟶ scribble

crumble	handle	idle	stifle
candle	nettle	rifle	fable
kettle	humble	stable	bridle

4 Choose 4 words from section 3 and write each in a sentence of your own in your exercise book.

5 📖 then follow track 8 for ⊚ ✎ or 💻.

1 The ducks waddle and paddle in the puddle.

2 The cattle stumble and trample on the long wet grass.

3 The horses were startled by the crackle of gunfire.

23. Reading comprehension: making waffles

Changing text into the past tense.

1

One day Daisy and Luke decide to make some
waffles. They had eaten them, smothered in warm
syrup and cream, when they were on holiday in
America. Now they want to try to make some
themselves.

Daisy mixes flour, milk and eggs. Luke greases the
electric waffle maker, which looks very much like
a sandwich maker. As soon as it is hot they start to
ladle some of the batter onto the griddle.

The mixture bubbles and sizzles as they close the lid.
Some of it dribbles onto the kitchen table. Luke wipes it up with a damp
cloth and then tickles Daisy with a corner of the soggy rag. She giggles
and flicks a bit of batter off the spoon onto Luke's cheek. Soon there
is a struggle taking place in the kitchen and the waffles are forgotten.
Suddenly Luke begins to sniff. He can smell charred pancake batter. The
waffles are a disaster. The smell brings their mother rushing into the
kitchen. She is not impressed. "The kitchen is a place for cooking," she
screams, "not tickling and tackling and dribbling batter."

2 Now write out the passage in section 1 in the past tense.

Use the past tense -ed ending for most verbs and change **is** to **was** and **are**
to **were**. Watch out for a place where **is** does not change.

3 Answer these questions in your exercise book. You may need to use the
dictionary to help you as the answers are not all in the passage.

1 What is a waffle?
2 Name three things mixed together to make batter
   (the pancake mixture).
3 Is it sensible to play games in the kitchen?
   Write a few sentences giving your reasons for your answer.

4
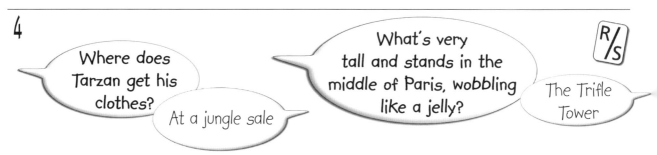

Where does Tarzan get his clothes?

At a jungle sale

What's very tall and stands in the middle of Paris, wobbling like a jelly?

The Trifle Tower

R/S

Write two sentences. Remember punctuation

1 Write 2 pieces of good advice for the situations.

e.g. I think I've got flu.   *Go home now.*
Go to bed with a hot water bottle.

1 My knees and legs really hurt after that long run.

2 We've run out of milk.

3 The dog needs to go for a walk.

4 He won't do his homework.

5 I need to lose weight.

2 Use the adjectives to write 2–3 sentences in your exercise book about 4 people you know.

e.g. Intelligent   *The most intelligent person I know is my dad.*
He helps me with my Maths homework.

1 friendly
2 sporty
3 kind
4 interesting

25. Consonant trigraph -TCH -tch -*tch*

1 Say **match** [ch])))).

Sna**tch** the ca**tch** to win the ma**tch**.

2 Trace and copy.

Watch the catch all the way.

3 Trace, add *tch* and read.

ca___	fe___	wi___	no___
twi___	wa___	pi___	ke___
Du___	scra___	clu___	blo___

4 Underline **-tch**. You should fine 9. Then 📖.

Jim went to fetch some fish and chips for supper. As it was dark he took his torch. There was a chill in the air so he clutched his coat around his chin.

When he got home again he undid the latch, switched on the light in the porch and took off his boots. He put his fish and chips on a plate and put ketchup on them.

After he had finished eating, he watched the match on TV for a bit. Then he scratched his head and got up, remembering that he had to feed his rabbit in its hutch.

More about -tch

1 then follow track 9 for or .

crutch   ditch

snatch   stretch

1 Dad made a sketch of Patch the dog.
2 A witch can make you itch and scratch if she puts a spell on you.
3 The children play catch and hopscotch in the park.

2 Complete this part of *Adventures of Isabel* by Ogden Nash.

Once in a night as black as pi_____

Isabel met a wicked old wi_____.

The wi_____'s face was cross and wrinkled.

The wi_____'s gums with teeth were sprinkled.

Ho ho, Isabel! the old wi_____ crowed,

I'll turn you into an ugly toad!

Isabel, Isabel didn't worry,

Isabel didn't scream or scurry,

She showed no rage and she showed no rancour,

But she turned the wi_____ into milk and drank her.

Read these lines aloud. Make the witch sound really frightening.
Make Isabel calm and matter of fact.

3 Write 2–3 sentences on the following:

1 What you usually have for breakfast.
2 What did you do at the weekend?
3 Describe the room that you are in now.

4

Why are football pitches sometimes wet?

Because footballers often like to dribble.

R/S

27. Punctuation: the comma

1 The comma separates words or groups of words from each other.
It is placed between items or words in a list, instead of **and**.
The words in the list can be nouns, verbs or adjectives.

e.g. Dad bought crisps and lemonade and chocolate and apples.
Dad bought crisps, lemonade, chocolate and apples.

2 Try making lists using commas. Copy and complete these sentences,
writing them in your exercise book. Try to list at least 4 items for each.

1 When I emptied the waste-paper basket I found _____

2 From the window of this room I can see _____

3 In the fridge we keep _____

4 When I get dressed I put on _____

3 Choose words from the boxes to describe the people in this story in an
interesting way. Remember to use commas.

young short in his 20s dark skinned hair black	I jumped on to the bus and collapsed into the nearest seat. I was sitting opposite a man. He was _____

old in her 70s grey curly hair short thin	At the next stop a woman struggled on to the bus. She was _____

in his 60s smelly bald dirty fat	The young man stood up and offered his seat to the frail old lady. Just at that moment a man pushed his way forward and sat down on it. He was _____

4 Track 10. ◎

1

The hedgehog has a wide range of habitat. It is most often seen on the fringes of woodland, on wasteland, near villages, or in parks and gardens. Hedgehogs are nocturnal animals. After spending the day sleeping under bushes or thick shrubs, they emerge at dusk and rummage around in hedge bottoms or verges for their supper.

The hedgehog is called the gardener's friend because it feeds on many pests such as caterpillars, slugs and baby mice. This is an advantage if you cultivate cabbages, as slugs can do a lot of damage. Hedgehogs like to drink milk, eat pet food and dine on hens' eggs, which they have to smash before they can gulp them down.

When the hedgehog is in danger, it rolls up into a little ball of spikes. Their prickly spines (of which they have about 5,000) provide a defence against animals such as foxes. Sadly, the spines do not protect them against the motorist and if you are travelling in the morning before many people are about you will often find them squashed by cars.

In the coldest months hedgehogs hibernate and live off their body fat. On sunny days they may wake up to forage for food, but they go back to their nests as soon as it gets cold again. They can preserve their body warmth by rolling up snugly in their nests.

Compost heaps are places hedgehogs may choose to rummage in before hibernation. If you have a garden shed with a dry space under it or even a good thick hedge, put down a loose heap of grass or hay in which the hedgehog can make a nest before hibernation. You could even use a box with an entrance tunnel. Put a black plastic bag over it with dry leaves or compost on top. If a hedgehog does move in, do not disturb it while it is hibernating.

2 Comprehension questions

1 How does the hedgehog protect itself against enemies?

2 Name one of the hedgehog's enemies.

3 The passage refers to the hedgehog coming out only at night.
   Which word describes animals that are active at night?

4 What kind of food does the hedgehog like to eat?

5 How do hedgehogs manage to stay alive during hibernation?

1 Say **girl** .

That g<u>ir</u>l came f<u>ir</u>st.

2 Underline all the **ir** words **outside** the circle and read them. Then read the other words **outside** the circle.

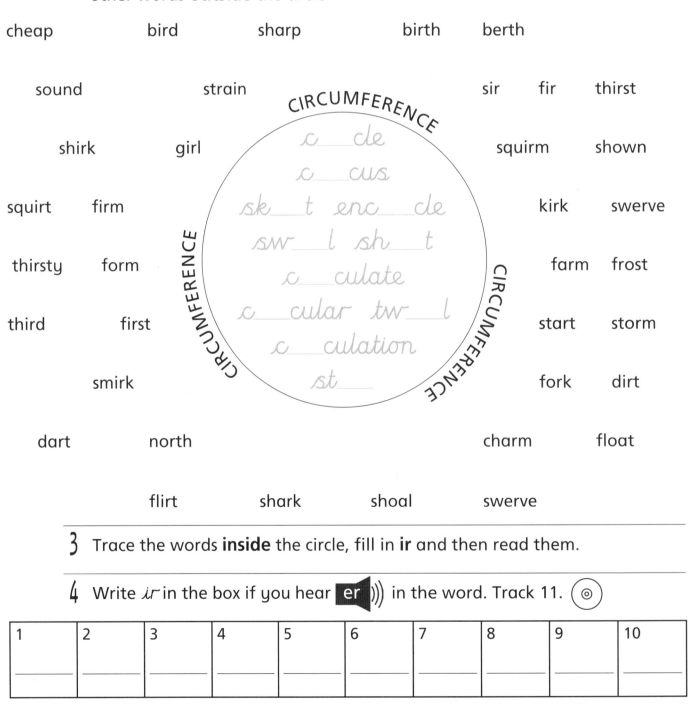

cheap   bird   sharp   birth   berth

sound   strain   sir   fir   thirst

shirk   girl   squirm   shown

squirt   firm   kirk   swerve

thirsty   form   farm   frost

third   first   start   storm

smirk   fork   dirt

dart   north   charm   float

flirt   shark   shoal   swerve

CIRCUMFERENCE

c__cle
c__cus
sk__t enc__cle
sw__l sh__t
c__culate
c__cular tw__l
c__culation
st__

3 Trace the words **inside** the circle, fill in **ir** and then read them.

4 Write *ir* in the box if you hear  in the word. Track 11. ◎

1	2	3	4	5	6	7	8	9	10
___	___	___	___	___	___	___	___	___	___

More about ir

1 📖 Read with the CD and number the words correctly. Track 12. ◎

☐	stir	☐	verse	☐	first	☐	shirt	☐	third
☐	thirsty	☐	thermal	☐	circle	☐	swerve	☐	term
☐	skirt	☐	herd	☐	thirst	☐	circulation		

2 📖 then ◎ ✎ or 💻. Track 13.

girl   first   circle
skirt   squirm   circus

1 There are thirteen dirty socks, skirts, shirts, vests and pairs of pants
  in the wash.
2 There is a small, pretty, brown bird chirping in the fir tree.
3 She will be thirty next birthday.

3 Can you solve this riddle?

No matter how long I keep going, I never get any further away
from one spot. I always end up where I began. My path is a _ _ _ _ _ _.

If you answer correctly, the letters in the boxes will help
you spell the solution.

	True	False
Some beautiful rings have stones made of carbon.	C	D
A star is a huge ball of hot, glowing gases, whirling in space.	I	A
The zone near the South Pole is called the Arctic.	T	R
The Earth is perfectly round.	T	C
The highest clouds are often made up of drops of ice.	L	M
Two of the best-known British migrating birds are the rook and the robin.	P	E

4

What's brown and prickly and squirts jam at you?

A hedgehog eating a doughnut.

What bird prepares food?

A cook-coo

R/S

31. Common confusions

1 Circle the correct spelling: **there**, **their** or **they're**.

e.g. *They're* / *There* / *Their* going to have a lovely time when they get *there* / *their* / *they're* and find *they're* / *there* / *their* hotel.

1 *There* / *Their* / *They're* not going to walk *there* / *their* / *they're* on *there* / *their* / *they're* own.

2 *They're* / *There* / *Their* going to watch *their* / *there* / *they're* team play on Saturday.

3 They will stay *there* / *their* / *they're* until *they're* / *their* / *there* ready to move to *their* / *there* / *they're* new home.

2 Circle the correct spelling: **your** or **you're**.

e.g. *Your* / *You're* too early. *Your* / *You're* appointment is at 10.15 a.m.

1 Where are *your* / *you're* gloves? *Your* / *You're* going to need them for the walk.

2 *Your* / *You're* going to love Venice. Is it *your* / *you're* first visit to Italy?

3 *Your* / *You're* playing for the first team on Saturday. You must do *your* / *you're* best.

3 Choose a suitable spelling: **your you're they're their there**

1 _____ going to miss him when he leaves _____ school.

2 _____ best friends will think _____ being silly.

3 _____ won't be any room in _____ car if _____ going to take all those people.

4 I can take _____ dog for a walk if _____ too tired to do it.

5 _____ are thirteen of them and _____ all going to come on _____ bikes.

4 (Sp) Ask your teacher for a spelling test.

Essential spellings

1 Work across. ⟶

Read	Trace, naming letters	Write
1 watch	*watch*	
2 separate	*separate*	
3 different	*different*	
4 world	*world*	
5 work	*work*	
6 sure	*sure*	
7 money	*money*	
8 impossible	*impossible*	
9 through	*through*	
10 sometimes	*sometimes*	

33. Vowel pattern UR ur *ur*

1 Say **nurse**

Don't h**ur**t me, n**ur**se!

2 Underline **ur**. You should find 11.

Thursdaymorningisurgentlyusedforburningrubbishensuringthatgermsado
neverturninthespurninghurtingtheherbsinurbanurnstrundlingcursorcurds

3 Trace, fill in *ur* and read.

Th___sday [ ]   c___ve [ ]   t___tle [ ]
b___st [ ]   ret___ning [ ]   sp___n [ ]
t___nip [ ]   b___ger [ ]
m___derer [ ]   dist___bing [ ]

Now count the number of syllables in each word and write it in the brackets after each word.

4 Write *ur* in the box if you hear **er** in the word. Track 14.

1	2	3	4	5	6	7	8	9	10

5

What's bad tempered and goes with custard?

Apple grumble

R/S

More about ur

1 Use the words in the right hand column to complete the sentences.

1 He _____ when he realised that he had a _____ tyre.	burst cursed
2 The little stream _____ and _____ on its way.	murmurs gurgles
3 The _____ took care not to _____ the _____ when he _____ for the jewels.	disturb furniture burglar returned
4 The _____ twisted and _____ as the _____ waves _____ him towards the shore.	hurled surfer turned surging

2 Underline the words which have the **ur** pattern. You should find 16.

Arthur was very badly burned and urgently required an operation.
Thanks to the skill of the surgeon and the help of the nurses, his injuries
soon stopped hurting and started to heal. By Thursday he was able to
return to his home in the suburb. As soon as he was better he purchased
new purple curtains and some sturdy furniture to replace what had been
burned. Most important of all, he installed a smoke alarm.

3 📖 then ⊙ ✎ or 💻 . Track 15.

turn	burning	disturb
curve	urgently	church

1 He will return by Thursday.
2 The purple balloon burst when he sat on it.
3 The nurse dropped his purse.

4 ✎ Write 2–3 sentences on the following in your exercise book:

1 Who uses the kitchen in your house and what do they do there?
2 Where did you go for your last holiday?
3 What are the train services like where you live?

35. Contractions: making words shorter

Writing it the way we say it.
An apostrophe (') is used to show that letters are missing.

1 Read and complete. The first 3 are done for you.

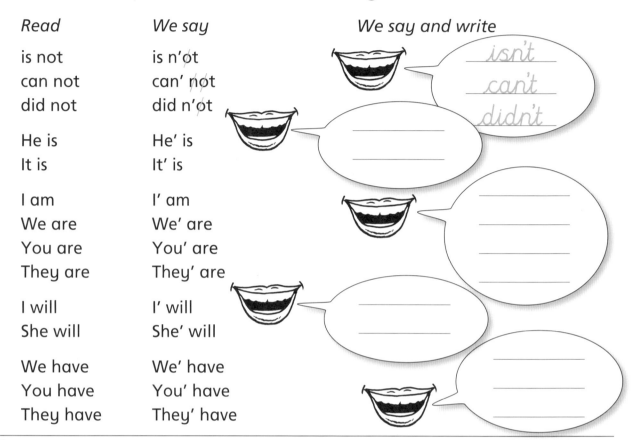

Read	We say	We say and write
is not	is n'ot	*isn't*
can not	can' n'ot	*can't*
did not	did n'ot	*didn't*
He is	He' is	
It is	It' is	
I am	I' am	
We are	We' are	
You are	You' are	
They are	They' are	
I will	I' will	
She will	She' will	
We have	We' have	
You have	You' have	
They have	They' have	

2 Note: 1 *Will not* is shortened to *won't*.
          2 *It's = it is;   its = of it* belonging to it

e.g. *It's* the bird which built *its* nest in the tree.

3 Rewrite these sentences, substituting the contraction for the underlined words.

1 He **is not** the first person who **cannot** spell.
2 James **has not** found his pen so he **cannot** complete his exercise.
3 **She is** going by bus but **we will** have to cycle.
4 **It is** always a frantic panic when **they have** overslept.
5 **They are** the drop-outs who would not attend college and now **they are** on probation.

Now try these using **should** and **would**.
6 You **should not** keep wild animals in captivity because they will seldom be happy.
7 They **could have** won the prize if **they had** practised harder.

Punctuation: using capital letters for proper nouns

1 Proper nouns are names of people, places, times and titles of books and films. They require capital letters at the beginning.

e.g. Names: Imran, Mrs Hudson, Professor Chang, Captain Anderson, Dr Ali
      Places: Pakistan, Sweden, Paris, New York, South China Sea, Caribbean
      Times: Tuesday, July, Ramadan, Thursday, August, Christmas, Divali
      Titles: *Daily Mail*, *News at Ten*, *Neighbours*, *Charlie and the Chocolate Factory*

Write out these sentences, using capital letters where required.
Add punctuation.

1 the jackson family left for swindon yesterday
2 madrid is the capital of spain
3 ibrahim enjoyed reading the latest harry potter book
4 ann boleyn was the second wife of henry viii
5 archy and george have gone to watch the arsenal match

---

2 Imagine you have done these things:

e.g. *lost something*   been on holiday   changed schools   moved house

Write 3–4 sentences about each in your exercise book.
Remember to use capital letters where appropriate.

e.g. *I lost my football socks last week. I wasn't allowed to play*
     in the Southport match. They turned up in Mike's kit bag.
     I don't know how they got there.

---

3 Sp Take these 18 cards from the Spelling/Reading pack.

Use them to make the words your teacher says to you.

37. Vowel pattern OY oy *oy*

1 Say **boy**  . **oy** occurs most often as a final syllable in words. It may also occur as the stressed syllable in longer words.

The b**oy** ann**oy**s R**oy**.

2 Trace and fill in *oy*. Read the words you have made with your teacher.

s__a____ r__al__ pl_____ empl_____

l__alty__ all_____ v__age__ destr_____

3 Write *oy* in the box if you hear  at the end of the word. Track 16. ◎

1	2	3	4	5	6	7	8	9	10

4 Fill in the grid. Use the words from section 2.

1 A cunning trick.

2 Mixture of 2 or more metals.

3 To give a job to someone.

4 To break or demolish.

5 To do with king or queen.

6 A kind of bean.

7 A trip, usually by sea.

8 Faithfulness.

More about oy

1 Underline or highlight the **oy** pattern in these words.

Put a ring round the odd one out in these groups. Read all the words.

1 e.g. coy joy (jay) toy

2 envoy replay enjoy convoy

3 annoy ahoy alloy away

4 Goya royal loyal relay

5 foyer employer player destroyer

6 destroy decay deploy decoy

---

2 📖 Read and underline the **oy** pattern. You should find 14.

The flamboyant Mr Doyle was standing in the foyer of the Savoy Hotel when he saw his pride and joy, his silver Rolls Royce, zoom past the door. He rushed out to see joy-riders driving towards the highway. He was so annoyed that he could no longer enjoy his dish of oysters and went to alert the police. They soon informed him that the car had been destroyed in a crash. The joy-riders, who were unemployed, were already at Croydon Police Station and under arrest.

---

3 Listen to the CD at track 17 (◎). Put a ring round the word you hear.

1 spout sprout

2 plaster plastic

3 cloud clout clown

4 optic option

5 play ploy

6 static station status

7 tittle title

8 joy jay

9 electric electrical electricity

10 faction frantic fraction

11 conversation conservation

12 witch with whisk

13 employed employing employer

14 Royce race rice

15 director direction directed

4

© Beat Dyslexia Book 5 LDA

39. Using adjectives to write interesting sentences

1 Choose adjectives from the box to describe the nouns in these sentences.

> convenient dark noisy quiet untidy dry wet cold hot empty

1 A house near a motorway is _____

2 A home which is close to the shops and railway station is

_____

3 A school room when the students are doing an exam is _____

4 A glass when you have drunk the last drop of orange juice is _____

2 Make this short passage interesting by choosing adjectives from the box to write in the blank spaces. Try to use more than one adjective in each space. Remember to use commas.

> front tree-lined narrow wooden country friendly stone-built new large pretty small heavy young

Lloyd walked down the _____ lane. He was searching for

his friend's home. He wandered past a _____ house, but he

could not find the number. He strode up to the _____ door

and rang the bell. A _____ woman opened it.

3 Write 2–3 sentences on the following:

1 Are you a healthy person? What do you do that is good for your health?
2 What is there for young people to do in your town in the evening or at weekends?
3 What do you prefer to do with your free time?

4 What do you call a boy who swims round in circles in rivers?

Eddy

Adding suffixes to words

Change for correct spellings.

1 Work across. ⟶

Read the word	Add -ing	Add -ed	Add -er
decide			
promote			
cry			
meddle			
divide			
produce			
employ			
love			
drop			
shuffle			
train			
supply			
rob			
clean			
squirt			
serve			
pray			
import			
pollute			
dine			

41. Vowel pattern OI oi *oi*

1 Say **coin** . **oi** occurs as the beginning or main syllable of a word.

"**Oi**, **oi**! Lend me a c**oi**n, mate."

---

2 Trace and fill in *oi*.

b___l *rec___led* *unav___dable*

sp___l *embr___dery* *disapp___ntment*

---

3 Write *oi* in the box if you hear **oy** in the word. Track 18.

1	2	3	4	5	6	7	8	9	10
___	___	___	___	___	___	___	___	___	___

---

4 Underline or highlight the **oi** pattern in these words.

1 join groin groan loin coin   3 joist moist foist joust

2 foil toil soil foal oil boil   4 choice voice rejoice chance

Read the **oi** words. Ring the odd word in each rhyming group.

5

What do you get
if you pour boiling water
down a rabbit's hole?

Hot cross bunnies

R/S

Punctuation: speech marks

More about oy and oi

1 Fill in *oi* or *oy* and read:

R_____, a builder, had had a bad day. He was on the b_____l and

sp_____ling for a fight. So when Tom Benton, his j_____ner, arrived late for

an app_____ntment with his empl_____er, R_____ was very ann_____ed.

" You're a sp_____lt, lazy b_____, Tom," stormed R_____ in a loud

v_____ce. "If you disapp_____nt me again I'll have no ch_____ce but to

sack you."

"I could help you h_____st that j_____st, R_____," said Tom, in a quiet

v_____ce, keen to av_____d the sack.

"That's not the p_____nt," said R_____n_____sily, beads of m_____sture

breaking out on his brow. He looked at Tom and could see that the

b_____y was a l_____al worker.

"Oh, go and shift that heap of top-s_____l," he said.

Study the passage above. Notice:
- that speech marks are only wrapped around the words which are actually spoken
- the position of full stops and commas when speech marks are closed
- that each time another person speaks a new line is used.

2 📖 then 💿✏️ or 💻. Track 19.

Try to use speech punctuation

annoy	oil
employ	soil
royal	joint

1 "What noise annoys an oyster?" asked the boy.
2 "A noisy noise annoys an oyster," replied Roy.
3 "Never put boiling oil into a plastic bottle," said Joyce in a loud voice.

43. Crossword fun OI

1 Read and then use these words to complete the crossword.

anoint	appointment	voice	toil	boil
poison	joiner	turquoise	avoid	tabloid
turmoil	spoil	exploit	poise	void
noise	loiter	coins	moist	point
ointment	oil	soil	goitre	hoist
				cloisters

Across

1 Agitation or state of disorder (7)
4 The sharp end of a tool or pencil (5)
7 Harmful substance (6)
9 Upper layer of ground, in which plants grow (4)
11 Swelling in the neck as a result of enlargement of the thyroid gland (6)
15 Arrangement to meet at a specific time and place (11)
17 To hang about or linger doing nothing (6)
19 Sound formed in the larynx, used for singing, shouting, speaking (5)
20 Work incessantly (4)
21 When a liquid starts to bubble up (4)
22 Raise by means of ropes (5)
23 Person who makes furniture and woodwork (6)

Down

1 A bluish stone (9)
2 Slightly wet or damp (5)
3 A bold or daring feat (7)
4 Composed manner (5)
5 Greasy healing preparation for the skin (8)
6 Keep away from a person or place (5)
8 A sound (5)
10 Covered walks in convents or cathedrals (9)
12 Popular newspaper with bold headlines (7)
13 Damage or allow to go bad (5)
14 Apply oil or ointment at ceremony (6)
16 Pieces of money (5)
18 To lubricate; petrol is refined from it (3)
19 Empty, vacant (4)

Adverbs

Suffix -ly

1 Adverbs tell how (or when or where) an action is done.
Underline or use a highlighter pen to pick out the adverbs
in these sentences.

e.g. 1 The man walked <u>briskly</u>. (How did he walk? <u>Briskly</u>)
2 The woman dressed smartly.
3 The witch cackled nastily.
4 The children sang sweetly.
5 The boy ate heartily.

2 Use your own choice of adverbs to describe how you do these activities.

carefully	quickly	slowly	promptly	rapidly	suddenly
lazily	deeply	happily	angrily	clumsily	gladly
sleepily	loudly	noisily	silently		

1 I wake up _____

2 I get out of bed _____

3 I eat my breakfast _____

4 I work _____

5 I listen _____

6 I play _____

7 I speak _____

8 I go home _____

9 I watch TV _____

10 I sleep _____

3 Adverbs can be formed from adjectives, but note the spelling change when
an adjective ends in **-y**.

e.g. *hungry* + *ly* = *hungrily*

The **-y** changes to **i** and then suffix **-ly** is added to make the adverb.

Write the adverbs in your exercise book.

wary   merry   lucky   pretty   shabby   thirsty   tidy   heavy

45. Long-vowel pattern IE ie *ie*

Colour the long-vowel pattern <u>red</u>.

1 Say **chief** . The sound is the same as alphabetical name **E**.

Good gr<u>ie</u>f! Big ch<u>ie</u>f!

2 Ring *ie*. You should find 7.

ochyielbisieladiemnpiesfjkielzeixiegriegu

3 Join the letters to write the words.

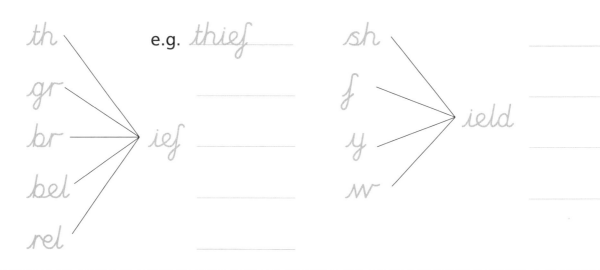

th   e.g. *thief*   sh

gr   f

br   *ief*   y   *ield*

bel   w

rel

4 Link the rhyming patterns.

e.g. grieves	fierce
believed	piece
frieze	chiefly
yielding	achieved
niece	thieves
pierce	shielding
briefly	sieze

More about ie

1 Underline or highlight all the words which have the **ie** pattern.
Read all the words.

siege	thieves	frieze	grieving	chief
reprieve	three	fiendish	yeast	repeat
hygienic	cheap	gum-shield	theme	relieved
believable	fierce	priest	shriek	yield
peach	niece	cheat	retriever	diesel

2 Use some of the words which were underlined in section 1 to complete these sentences.

1 This truck runs on _____ , not petrol.

2 The _____ of police was _____

   to hear that his force had escaped the latest terrorist attack.

3 My _____ always wears a _____

   when she is playing hockey.

4 The _____ family were comforted by their Roman

   Catholic _____ .

5 A golden _____ is not a very _____ dog.

6 Although they had been under _____ for three months,

   the people inside the castle would not _____ to the

   invading troops.

7 The report that the judge had granted a _____ to the

   violent _____ was frankly un_____ .

8 She decorated the walls of her room with an attractive

   _____ .

3

What did the priest say when he saw insects on his flowers?

Let us spray.

47. Conjunctions

Words used to join simple sentences.

1 Use the words in the box to join 2 simple sentences together to make a more interesting sentence. Each word may be only used once. Fill in the conjunction on the line and number the second part to match the first one. Don't forget to change the punctuation.

and	if	although
	but	because
when	unless	so

e.g. 1 He ran to catch the bus. _but_ ⬜ She loved drinking coke.

2 You will cut your finger. _____ ⬜ I had to change my clothes.

3 She enjoyed eating pancakes. _____ [1] He was just too late.

4 I was caught in a storm. _____ ⬜ You are not careful.

5 We shall not pass our exams. _____ ⬜ He broke the rules.

6 He was severely punished. _____ ⬜ We revise carefully.

7 She was expected to work. _____ ⬜ He saved the children.

8 He was rewarded for bravery. _____ ⬜ She was only eight years old.

2 Conjunctions can be used at the beginning of the sentence. Note the need for a comma.

e.g. He had a cold. He still went to school …
Although he had a cold, he still went to school.

Complete this exercise as you did in section 1, but this time place the conjunction at the beginning of the sentence.

Choose from: **although if when unless**.

1 _____ He had eaten his meal. ⬜ He will incur annoyanc

2 _____ She is awarded a grant. ⬜ He did the washing up

3 _____ He changes his attitude. ⬜ She still swam 20 lengths a day.

4 _____ She was over 80. ⬜ She will go to universit

More about conjunctions

Interesting sentences

1 Use the words in the box to join these ideas.
You can change the order of the ideas.

and   so   but
although   as
because

   1 It's an old bike.
     It goes fast.
     I've done lots of work on it.

   2 It's only a small caravan.
     It has everything we need.
     We have been everywhere in it.

   3 It's a very small village.
     It's easy to get to know everyone.
     People are very friendly.

2 Improve the passage by adding these conjunctions
to make more interesting sentences.

Change the punctuation.

and   because
when   so
although   but

I once spent a wonderful day beside a rushing river in the
north of Scotland. We picnicked on the short grass. We passed
the time relaxing in the sunshine. We chose a spot near a
waterfall. We wanted to watch the salmon leaping. The signal
that it was time for some action came. We noticed a crowd
starting to gather on the platform overhanging the waterfall.
The water was crystal clear. We could observe the amazing
creatures swimming purposefully upstream over the pebbles.
Suddenly we would see a flash of wriggling silver as a brave
female flung herself up over the rapids. She dashed herself on
the rocks as she fought the current. This did not deter her. Often
she would be washed back down to the start again. She would
land just short of the pool above. It might take several attempts.
Usually she would succeed. We hoped she would reach her
spawning ground to lay her eggs.

49. Long-vowel pattern IE ie *ie*

Colour the long-vowel pattern red.

1 Say **pie** 🔊. The sound is the same as alphabetical name I.

This pie chart shows how Floyd spent £1.20.

40p comic
10p bus
20p drink
20p sweets
30p saved

Make a pie chart to show how he spent £2.40.

A p**ie**ce of p**ie**.

2 📖 die tie pie lie fie   magpies vie untie belie died

3 Note the spelling of these plurals.

cry loud cries   spy two spies   sky blue skies   fly many flies

4 Use some of the words from section 2 to complete these sentences.

1 Did Floyd tell a _____?
2 Can you _____ his shoe laces, please?
3 The lads _____ with each other to see who is the strongest.
4 He _____ in a train crash last year.
5 One for sorrow, two for joy. Those birds are _____.
6 Do you like pumpkin _____?

5 Listen to the words on the CD and write them in the correct column. Track 20. ◎

-y	-igh	-ie

6 *Did you hear about the two flies playing football in a saucer?*

They were practising for the cup.

R/S

A		
E		
I		ie
O		
U		

© Beat Dyslexia Book 5 LDA

Essential spellings

1 Work across. ⟶

Read	Trace, naming letters	Write
1 enough	*enough*	
2 original	*original*	
3 believe	*believe*	
4 family	*family*	
5 happily	*happily*	
6 probably	*probably*	
7 building	*building*	
8 although	*although*	
9 quietly	*quietly*	
10 definite	*definite*	

     Permission to Photocopy

51. Writing sentences and making sense

1 ✎ Write sentences to describe the following.

1 a computer
2 an alarm clock
3 a refrigerator
4 a vacuum cleaner
5 a toaster

2 ✎ Choose 1 from each section and write a sentence to describe what it is like.

1 barge trawler canoe ferry life-boat
yacht container-ship liner

2 motor-bike car lorry van taxi bus
coach tanker tractor

3 hotel bungalow house castle palace
cottage motel flat

4 cat dog horse budgerigar goldfish
hamster guinea-pig rabbit

5 lion giraffe hippopotamus elephant
crocodile zebra cheetah

3 A sentence is a group of words which make sense. Too often sentences do not make sense. Is this your problem? A reader shouldn't have to re-read a passage in order to understand it. For example this student was writing about school lunches.

The second thing is school lunches. They sell the nicer tasting more healthier food for more money than the junk food. This means for the more poor people they will not be able to eat healthy like other people and also while we are talking about money they do not let you borrow money for people who are short of it and who have forgotten it.

Rewrite this passage in your exercise book so that it makes sense. You may make as many changes as you like to the words and sentences in order to achieve clarity.

Looking at words with prefixes and suffixes

1 Read these words. Now choose the prefix *re-*, *dis-* or *ex-* and write it at the beginning of each word to change its meaning.

grace   *plain*   *main*

array   *claim*   *play*

train   *place*   *pay*

2 Read the words and then underline the prefixes.

e.g. unequal   concave   mischief   injustice

      explain   illegal   impossible   interact

      superimpose   proposition   irregular   disloyal

3 Trace and add consonant suffixes *-ful*, *-ly*, *-ment*, *-ness* to the end of these words.

hope   *bold*   *excite*   *slow*

narrow   *boast*   *happy*   *close*

still   *enrol*   *shallow*   *enjoy*

4 Add vowel suffixes *-ing*, *-er*, *-able*, *-ed* to these words and write the word you make on the line below. Remember silent e spelling rules. Read the words.

advise   light   move   ride

prize   avoid   drive   entwine

desire   believe   decide   frighten

5 (Sp) Ask your teacher for a spelling test.

53. Vowel digraph AU au *au*

1 Say **sauce** aw))).

Astron**au**ts like s**au**ce!

2 Write *au* in the box if you hear aw))) in the word. Track 21. ◉

1	2	3	4	5	6	7	8	9	10

3 Underline *au* and then read with your teacher.

sauce   fauna   maul   auburn   haunts   gaunt   jaunt

haulage   launch   caused   because   jaundice   applause

autumn   laundry   gaudy   gauze

4 Complete these sentences by filling in words from section 3.

1 They will _____ the rocket at the beginning of the

_____ in order to make use of the best weather conditions.

2 The audience gave the performers a loud round of _____ .

3 The memory of the accident he _____ still _____ Paul.

4 You need biological detergent to remove tomato _____ stains

in your _____ .

More about au

1 Underline or highlight the word you hear. Track 22.

1 sound   launch   sauce   lunch   loud
2 pause   clause   cloud   flaunt   flounce
3 paunch   pounce   laundry   foundry   launder
4 applause   applied   around   automatic   autocratic
5 taut   tout   trout   hound   haunt

2 Write these headings in your exercise book: *ou au.*

Listen to the CD and write the words you hear under the correct heading.

You should finish with 5 words under each heading. Track 23. ◎

3 📖 Read these instructions for making a curry.

Circle all the ingredients and also all the accompaniments.
In your exercise book make 1 list of ingredients and 1 list of
accompaniments, based on the words you have circled.
Remember to use commas between items in the lists.

Chicken curry
Method: Heat 60g of margarine and fry a finely chopped onion and an
apple. Stir until soft. Stir in 1 tablespoon of flour and 1 tablespoon of curry
powder. Cook gently for several minutes. Add 500g of diced chicken and
continue to fry gently. Add 0.5 litre of chicken stock gradually and bring
to the boil. When the stock has thickened, add a pinch of salt, some pepper
and a teaspoon of sugar. Then add 1 dessertspoon of desiccated coconut,
1 tablespoon of sultanas, 1 tablespoon of chutney and a few drops of
vinegar or lemon. Simmer for about 30 minutes.

Boiled rice is usually served as an accompaniment to a curry dish.
Poppadums or chapatti bread are also served. Some people like sliced
banana or chutney with a curry. Tomatoes and yoghurt with cucumber
are also popular.

4 Note these words. Highlight **gh**.

gh is silent: caught   taught   haughty   naughty   daughter   slaughter
Odd word: laugh – ha ha!

> When does
> an astronaut have
> his midday meal?

> At launch time

55. Writing clearly and making sense

1 📖 Answer in complete, accurate sentences.

Write the sentences in your exercise book.

e.g. 1 Why does a football boot have studs?
A football boot has studs so that the player does not slip.

2 Why does a spider spin a web?

3 Why does an apple have pips?

4 Why does a giraffe have a long neck?

5 How does an umpire start a cricket match?

6 What do you do before posting a letter?

7 What do you do for a friend's birthday?

8 What do you do before getting on a train?

9 Why do birds build nests?

10 Why do cows eat grass?

11 Why does a car have windscreen wipers?

12 What should you do if you cut your hand?

13 How do you spend your pocket money?

14 How do you find out the meaning of a word?

2 ✏ Use short sentences to write instructions.

Each short sentence tells people what to do next.

1 Washing the games kit.

2 Going to bed.

e.g. Feeding the dog
Get the bag of dog food from the cupboard.
Check the dog bowl is clean.
Wash the dog bowl if it is not clean.
Put the dog food in the bowl.
Call the dog.
Check he has eaten his food.

Prepositions

A preposition joins a noun to the rest of a sentence.

1 Listen to the instructions on the CD to complete the pictures. Track 24.

1 above	2 across	3 after	4 behind	5 between

6 under	7 into	8 towards	9 at	10 on

2 Fill in the correct preposition.

1 Everyone was invited to the party _____ the twins.

2 Pupils are not permitted to talk _____ the examination.

3 She was arrested _____ members of the police force.

4 He had to get up _____ the sun came up.

5 He cycled _____ the woods on his way to work.

6 The pupils protested _____ the detention.

about
by
through
before
except
during

3 Listen to the CD. Write the correct preposition under each picture.

Track 25. Choose from the possibilities below.

with   beneath   in   behind   on   through   from   over   under   near

1	2	3	4	5

				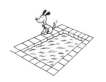
6	7	8	9	10

57. Vowel digraph AW aw *aw*

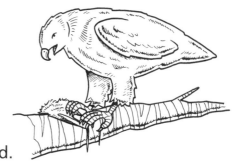

1 Say **claw** 🔊)))。

A h**aw**k's **aw**ful cl**aw**s can dr**aw** blood.

2 Tick the words you hear. Track 26. ◎

¹ cow	caw	² saw	sow	³ drawn	drown	⁴ raw	row	⁵ owning	awning
☐	☐	☐	☐	☐	☐	☐	☐	☐	☐
⁶ bowl	bawl	⁷ dawn	down	⁸ awe	owe	⁹ law	low	¹⁰ brown	brawn
☐	☐	☐	☐	☐	☐	☐	☐	☐	☐

3 📖 Read these words to your teacher.

withdrawn	dawdle	awkward	trawler	frogspawn
lawnmower	crawling	coleslaw	hawthorn	paw paw
strawberry	sawdust	unlawful	sprawling	squaw

4 Choose from the words above to answer the clues and fill in the grid.

1 Fishing vessel
2 Extremely quiet and reserved
3 Feeling embarrassed or clumsy
4 Tropical fruit
5 Moving slowly on all fours
6 Cuts the garden grass
7 Winter salad
8 Against the law
9 Bush or tree which flowers in May
10 Red summer fruit
11 Shavings from chopped wood
12 Lying with legs and arms flung out.

More about aw

1 📖 then 💿 ✏️ or 💻. Track 27.

  1 Raw prawns should be boiled before eating.
  2 The tawny owl swooped swiftly and caught the mouse with its claws.
  3 He scrawled his name on the picture he had drawn.

2 ✏️ Copy the headings Nouns and Adjectives into your exercise book.

Listen to the words on the CD and write them in the correct columns.

Track 28. 💿

Nouns	Adjectives
e.g. *audience*	*audible*

3 ✏️ Listen to the CD and complete the following sentences. Track 29. 💿

  1 He insists he _____ a flying _____ last _____ night.

  2 The Japanese love _____ squid dipped in horse-radish _____ .

  3 No one _____ what _____ to become extinct.

  4 The _____ coming from _____ car is against the _____ .

  5 The _____ attended the _____ of his latest book and
    agreed to sign copies of the first edition for the _____ .

  6 I love _____ but I have never tasted mango or _____ .

  7 The children _____ the _____ when fishing in the river.

  8 _____ is a disease of the liver and _____ of
    the skin.

  9 _____ went to _____ for a part in the pantomime.

  10 A lovely _____ covered her _____ shoulders.

4 Arrange the following words in dictionary order in your exercise book.

  saucer count propel crease cavern caught

59. Writing for a purpose: a postcard

Here is a postcard which Lucy sent to her parents, Roger and Jane Bainbridge, from a holiday campsite in France.

> 2.3.08
>
> We arrived at the campsite just in time for a swim before supper. It's a lovely place. Yesterday we went by train to Grenoble and tonight there is a party. There are many friendly people and it's very relaxing.
> See you soon.
> Love Lucy

> Mr and Mrs R. Bainbridge
> 6 Ridgeway Park
> Reading
> United Kingdom
> RG1 2PN

Pretend you are on holiday.

Think about the sporting activities you have taken part in, e.g. swimming, diving, cycling, playing tennis, riding. Think about the places you have visited, e.g. local villages or cities, farms, a zoo, a park.

Think about the people you are with or have met. Think about the food and the weather. Is it hot and sunny, or is it windy, breezy and gusty? Is it stormy, wet and rainy, or cold, damp or dull?

Tell a friend or your parents about your holiday.

Write your message on the left of the card and the name and address of the person or people you are writing to on the right. Remember to write the date in numbers.

1

It was on the return to base camp that things began to go wrong. Jason fell off the edge of a precipice. Luckily he landed on soft bushes covering a ledge beneath. He soon realised that he had broken his ankle and he was in much pain. Duncan was lowered down to him with first aid and then they managed to lift him back to the trail. They had to carry him while looking for somewhere to camp.

In the panic that had followed his fall, they had lost their compass and their way. Food supplies were beginning to dwindle. Luckily Rory had his emergency pocket book with him. Here are some of the things he read which helped them make it home safely.

Food: Preserve supplies. Collect edible berries or plants. Use snare wire, fish hooks and line, matches and the magnifying glass (for making a fire) from the emergency pack. Follow instructions to make a dead-fall trap.

A shelter should be high enough to sit in. Scoop out a hollow in the earth and put a low wall of stones round the edge of it. Fill the spaces between the stones with mud and leaves. Cut down saplings and weave them together to make a roof frame. Throw the tent or sheet over the top.

Fire provides warmth, protection and a means of signalling for help. It heats water, and cooks and preserves food. You must be able to light a fire in any conditions. Use a magnifying glass and dry grass in sunny conditions. Save your matches. Prepare a fireplace so you can control the fire. Choose a sheltered site. Clear away leaves, twigs and dry grass until you have bare earth. Collect tinder and kindling. Make a platform of green logs or a layer of stones if the ground is wet.

Messages: The international distress signal is: SOS. A flare signal is: red.
A sound signal is: 3 short blasts, 3 long blasts, 3 short.
A light signal is: 3 short flashes, 3 long flashes, 3 short.
A pilot in a plane will respond as follows. Message understood: tipping wings from side to side (daylight) or flashing green lights (at night).
Message not understood: flying plane in right-hand circle (daylight); flashing red lights (at night).

2 Questions

1 Who fell off the precipice?
2 What did the group lose in the panic following the fall?
3 Why is a magnifying glass a useful item in emergency supplies?
4 Describe how you would build a temporary shelter.
5 Why is it important to be able to light a fire?
6 Use your imagination to give 3 ways in which you might send a distress signal.

61. Consonant digraph PH ph *ph*

1   Say **photo** 🔊.

<u>Ph</u>ilip has a **ph**oto of So**ph**ie.

2   Underline or highlight **ph** as you read these words. Write the number of syllables in the box.

e.g. hy<u>ph</u>en [2] physics [ ] pheasant [ ] hemisphere [ ]

phial [ ] typhoon [ ] phosphate [ ] cacophony [ ]

lymph [ ] pamphlet [ ] amphibian [ ] autobiography [ ]

telegraph [ ] phrase [ ] phobia [ ] sapphire [ ]

sphinx [ ] pharmacy [ ] prophet [ ] graph [ ]

philosophy [ ] aphid [ ] emphasis [ ] epitaph [ ]

3   Find 16 words from section 2 in the word search.

f	l	n	t	p	p	m	c	a	c	o	p	h	o	n	y	q
x	y	j	s	h	h	q	l	z	e	p	i	t	a	p	h	d
z	m	m	p	o	o	t	e	b	q	k	f	g	r	a	p	h
t	p	x	h	b	s	x	a	m	p	h	i	b	i	a	n	j
y	h	s	i	i	p	a	w	j	p	h	y	s	i	c	s	y
p	p	h	n	a	h	p	h	i	l	o	s	o	p	h	y	p
h	h	e	x	e	a	h	p	r	o	p	h	e	t	a	p	h
o	k	u	v	z	t	i	j	p	e	n	h	e	w	t	q	i
o	p	m	f	m	e	d	p	h	a	r	m	a	c	y	u	a
n	a	u	t	o	b	i	o	g	r	a	p	h	y	h	o	l

Write the words you have found in your exercise book. Look up any words you do not know in your dictionary and write the definitions beside the words you have written.

4   Write the words you hear in your exercise book under these headings. Track 30. ◎

f   *ff*   *ph*   *gh*

1 Complete each **ph** word next to its definition.
  Use the dictionary if you are unsure of a word.

sphere	ph_____	1	Ghost
radiography	____ph_____	2	Globe
philanthropy	_____ph_____	3	Motherless and fatherless
geography	_____ph____	4	Large land-based mammal
biography	_____ph____	5	Use for communication
orphan	_____ph____	6	Air surrounding the planet
microphone	_____ph__	7	Study of the world
elephant	_____ph__	8	Change of form, e.g. tadpole to frog
ephemeral	_____ph__	9	Obtaining X-ray pictures
alphabet	_____ph__	10	Study of the statistics of birth, deaths, etc.
telephone	_____ph__	11	Written account of person's life
decipher	_____ph____	12	Makes the voice louder
dolphin	_____ph____	13	Decode
phantom	_____ph_____	14	Friendly sea creature
demography	____ph_____	15	All the letters
atmosphere	____ph_____	16	Lasting only a short time
metamorphosis	ph_____	17	Love of mankind

2 📖 and fill in *ph*.

Jose_____ claimed his tro_____y and then strode to the micro_____one
he uttered a few _____rases of trium_____ on behalf of the team the
atmos_____ere was _____enomenal afterwards he signed autogra_____
books as the press took _____otogra_____s next day the newspaper ran
paragra_____s on this tele_____onist who once lived in an or_____anage
but whose _____ysical strengths have made him a great football star he
plans to write his autobiogra_____y

Now correct the punctuation. You should find 6 sentences.

3   How can you tell
    if there's an elephant   You can't get
    in your oven?   the door shut.

63. Writing in paragraphs

Use the pictures to help you write a short story in 4 paragraphs.

A paragraph is a group of sentences about the same subject or idea. Each paragraph starts on a new line.

Imagine you have unexpectedly come into possession of a large amount of money. Write an introductory paragraph to explain how you came by this. Did you win it in a lottery or a competition, or from a premium bond? Or did you find it somewhere? Perhaps you inherited it from a wealthy relative or friend. In the next paragraph describe what you decided to do with the money. Use the third paragraph to describe what you purchased for yourself. Give as much detail as you can about what you bought and why you bought it. In the fourth and final paragraph, describe the gifts you bought for all your family and your friends. Use the pictures and words to help you recount how you went about doing this. Where did you go to buy the gifts? Did someone come with you or was it a surprise?

Use the words and pictures to help you recount what you decided to do.

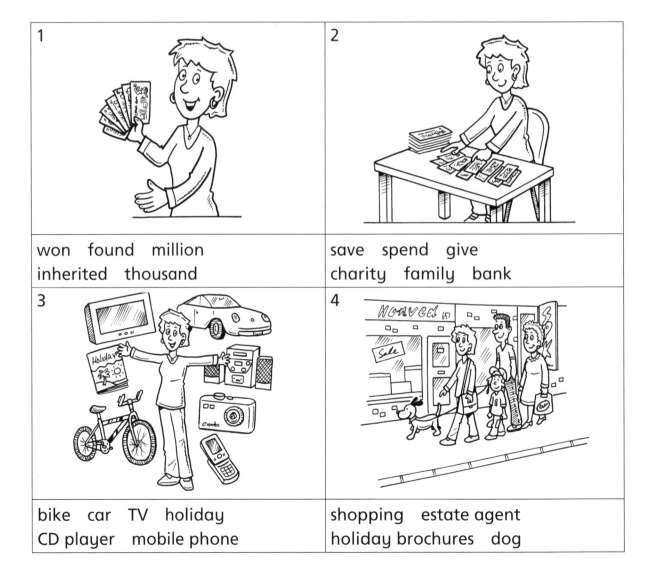

1 won found million inherited thousand	2 save spend give charity family bank
3 bike car TV holiday CD player mobile phone	4 shopping estate agent holiday brochures dog

Rules for plurals

Just add 's'	Change y to i and add -es	Change f to v and add -es	Add -es to words ending in tch, x, sh or ss, and -es to some words which end in o	Irregular
	e.g.: baby – babies sky – skies	e.g.: life – lives		
e.g.: job – jobs way – ways radio – radios page – pages	Do not change y to i if y follows a vowel e.g.: boy – boys	There are some exceptions e.g.: cliff – cliffs roof – roofs	e.g.: dishes hutches boxes potatoes dresses	e.g.: mouse – mice foot – feet tooth – teeth ox – oxen sheep – sheep man – men child – children

	Singular	Plural	Singular	Plural
e.g.	daisy	*daisies*	witch	
	leaf		brush	
	tomato		lady	
	topic		hero	
	child		wife	
	fox		toy	
	spy		hound	
	wish		shelf	
	nappy		louse	
	play		fairy	
	match		index	
	mystery		fraction	
	loaf		tragedy	
	ceremony		cosmetic	
	reply		question	

65. Long-vowel pattern EW ew *ew*

Colour the long-vowel pattern red.

1 Say **stew** .

The cr**ew** hate st**ew**!

2 Copy the following sentence twice in your exercise book.
Tick the one your prefer.

"Phew!" gasped my nephew Andrew, as he drew
a deep breath and blew up the last balloon.

3 Trace, filling in *ew*, and then read.

d___ f___ n___ h___ p___ y___

m___ st___ sp___ sk___ vi___ curl___

p___ter curf___ ren___ mild___ neph___

4 📖 then ◎ 🖉 or 🖥. Track 31.

curfew   drew   yew   Hebrew   jewel   chew

1 The curlew flew over the grassy dale.
2 My nephew pointed to the view.
3 There were a few pewter mugs for sale.
4 The crew pulled down the sails as the gale grew stronger and blew hard.

The apostrophe + s ('s) is used to show ownership or possession.

e.g. The bone belonging to (owned by) the dog = The dog's bone
The book belonging to (owned by) the student = The student's book

Use the apostrophe but keep the meaning.

e.g. 1 The land belonging to the farmer. *The farmer's land.*

2 The necklace owned by Yasmin. _____

3 The cat belonging to Dick Whittington. _____

4 The horse owned by the king. _____

5 The ears of the horse. _____

6 The paws of my dog. _____

7 The beak of the parrot. _____

8 The clothes bought for my sister. _____

9 The tools given to the workman. _____

10 The nose of the clown. _____

Change the apostrophe + s ('s) form into the longer form.

e.g. 1 Patrick's silkworms. _____

2 Jennifer's trumpet. _____

3 The soldier's boots. _____

4 The lion's mane. _____

67. Long-vowel pattern Ei ei *ei*

Colour the long-vowel pattern <u>red</u>.

EI

1 Say **reindeer** A))). The sound is the same as alphabetical name A.

The r<u>ei</u>ndeer pulls the w<u>ei</u>ght of the sl<u>ei</u>gh.

2 Trace and fill in *ei*. 📖

n___ghbours   ___ghteen   fr___ght   g___sha

b___ge   surv___llance   f___gn   n___ghs

Look up any words you do not know in the dictionary.

3 Listen to these words and sentences and number the word you hear.
Track 32. ◎

reign ☐	vane ☐	weight ☐	vein ☐	eight ☐	veil ☐
their ☐	way ☐	ate ☐	vain ☐	rain ☐	wait ☐
there ☐	vale ☐	sleigh ☐	reins ☐	weigh ☐	slay ☐

4 Complete the following sentences using words from sections 2 and 3.

1 The _____ of Queen Victoria lasted for 63 years.

2 After _____ years living next door to us, our _____ are moving.

3 At _____ kilos, that man is seriously over-_____.

4 The _____ train carries a load of chemicals.

5 A _____ carries blood back to the heart.

5

If a waiter was carrying a turkey on a platter and he dropped it, what three great disasters would occur?

The downfall of Turkey, the breaking up of China and the overthrow of Greece.

R/S

A	*ei*		
E			
I			
O			
U			

Writing in paragraphs

Use the pictures to help you write a short report in 6 paragraphs.

One day you were walking down the street when you witnessed an attempted robbery at a computer store. The police asked you for a statement. Write your report for the police in 6 paragraphs, including as much detail as you can and using the 6 pictures and the words below to help you.

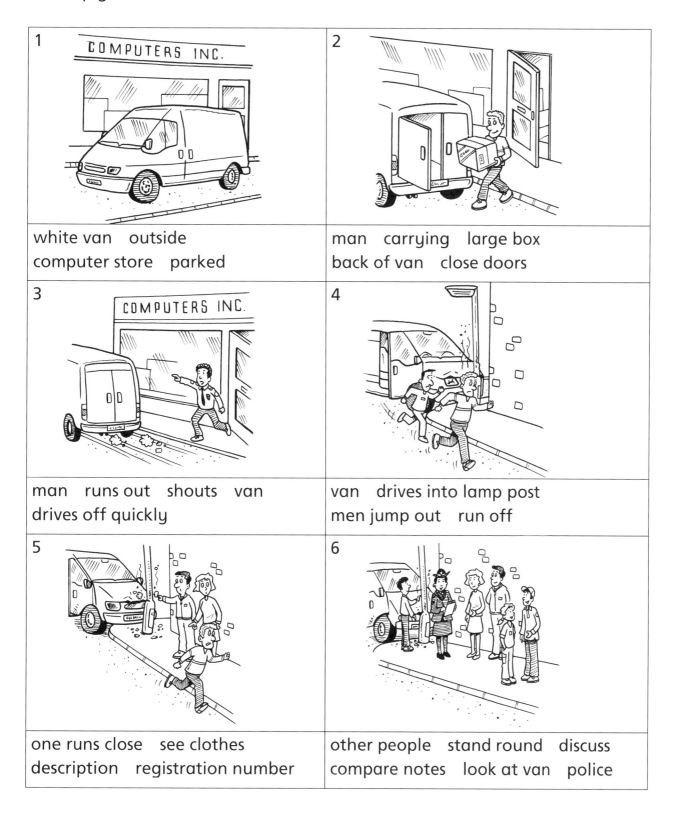

1 COMPUTERS INC.

white van   outside
computer store   parked

2

man   carrying   large box
back of van   close doors

3 COMPUTERS INC.

man   runs out   shouts   van
drives off quickly

4

van   drives into lamp post
men jump out   run off

5

one runs close   see clothes
description   registration number

6

other people   stand round   discuss
compare notes   look at van   police

69. Long-vowel pattern -UE -ue -ue

Colour the long-vowel pattern <u>red</u>.

1 Say **argue** .

Don't arg<u>ue</u> over the gl<u>ue</u>!

2

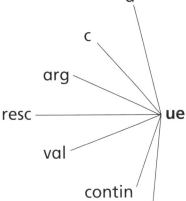

d
c
arg
resc —— **ue**
val
contin
stat

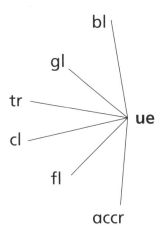

bl
gl
tr
cl —— **ue**
fl
accr

3 Ring *ue*. You should find 6.

tenorueglzuepluripueaquebifcjtduehkmues

4 Listen and write the number of each word in the box. Track 33.

mule ☐	tube ☐	rule ☐	flute ☐	duke ☐	June ☐
chew ☐	yew ☐	drew ☐	skew ☐	flew ☐	Jew ☐
hue ☐	argue ☐	blue ☐	true ☐	due ☐	clue ☐

5

What did the man say when he robbed the glue factory?

This is a stick-up!

More about -ue

1 📖 then 💿✏️ or 💻. Track 34.

rescue   value

argue   continue

clue   blue

1 I haven't a clue if that is true.
2 They painted the statue blue.
3 Why argue about the value of the Queen's jewels?

2 Use your dictionary to find the meanings of these words and use each in an interesting sentence:

accrue   venue   revenue   retinue   residue   pursue

3 Write the word and choose its 3 synonyms (words which mean the same) from the box below.

e.g. true   = accurate, authentic, correct

accrue   = _____ , _____ , _____

venue   = _____ , _____ , _____

revenue = _____ , _____ , _____

retinue   = _____ , _____ , _____

residue   = _____ , _____ , _____

| location income attendants followers accumulate place escort |
| deposit whereabouts profits amass takings dregs collect sediments |

4 🆂🅿 Ask your teacher for a spelling test.

5

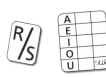

71. Listening for long-vowel sounds

1 Listen to the long-vowel sounds in these words. Write the word in the correct box according to the long-vowel sound you hear.
Track 35.

A)))	A)))
1 cake	tail
2	
3	
4	

A)))	E)))	E)))
1 tray	cream	queen
2		
3		
4		

E)))	I)))
1 chief	smile
2	
3	
4	

I)))	I)))	O)))
1 night	cry	nose
2		
3		
4		

O)))	O)))
1 snow	goat
2	
3	
4	

U)))	U)))	U)))
1 tube	stew	argue
2		
3		
4		

2 Now cut out the words and stick them onto card. You can use them to play Family Fours. See the teacher's notes (p.xvi).

Spider diagram

A way to plan stories and essays

1 Use the spider diagram to help you write stories. It will help you:

- get your ideas together – just let one idea trigger another and jot them down before you forget
- plan your story – you will have a note of all the good ideas you want to keep. You can also decide which ideas to leave out before you start to write.

You can use question words as prompts if you are stuck for ideas. Try answering the questions *Which*? *What*? *Where*? *When*? *Who*? *How*? and noting your answers.

Once you have noted your ideas, use the spider diagram to structure your story by putting your points or ideas in paragraph order.

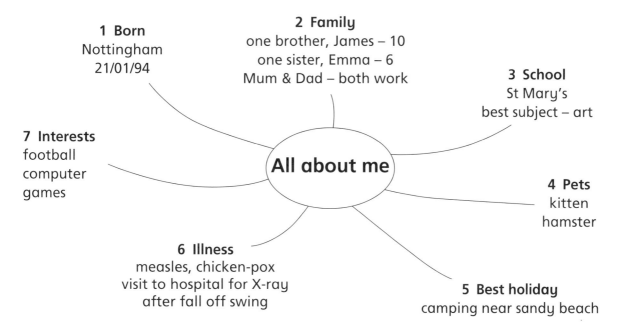

1 Born
Nottingham
21/01/94

2 Family
one brother, James – 10
one sister, Emma – 6
Mum & Dad – both work

3 School
St Mary's
best subject – art

7 Interests
football
computer
games

All about me

4 Pets
kitten
hamster

6 Illness
measles, chicken-pox
visit to hospital for X-ray
after fall off swing

5 Best holiday
camping near sandy beach

2 **Now make your own spider diagram.** Discuss your chosen subject with your teacher before you start. Remember it is always easiest to write from personal experience. You could choose from these topics:

- The time of my life – the best holiday you have ever had
- Losing a friend – a time when you moved to a new place, or a friend had to move.

Make as many notes as you can. Then decide which is going to be your opening paragraph, what will follow and how you will end. Number your ideas in paragraph order. You should aim for about 300 words, but the length can be greater.

73. Vowel suffix -OUS -ous -ous

1 Say **dangerous** (u))) (s))) . **-ous** is a vowel suffix that is added
to a noun to make an adjective meaning 'full of',
e.g. That quarry is a **danger** (noun) to children.
It is a **dangerous** (adjective) quarry.

Danger**ous**, venom**ous** snakes

2 As you listen to these words number the first word you hear [1]
and the second word you hear [2] in the brackets and so on. Track 36. (◎)

generous [ ]   famous [ ]   venomous [ ]   ridiculous [ ]
marvellous [ ]   tremendous [ ]   jealous [ ]   poisonous [ ]
adventurous [ ]   treacherous [ ]

3 Trace, filling in *ous*.

pomp___   fabul___   seri___   furi___

enorm___   nerv___

4 Fill in at least 1 **ous** word from section 2 or 3 above in each sentence.
Complete the unfinished sentences in your exercise book, using your
own ideas.

  1 Which are the most _____ quicksands or avalanches?
  2 There, in the undergrowth, lurked a _____ snake.
  3 He looked utterly _____ in his fancy dress costume, which
     consisted of …
  4 The elephant looked _____ when compared with …
  5 He had a _____ benefactor who gave him a grant to start …
  6 It was a _____ idea to …
  7 Footballers, snooker players and … have all become more
     _____ since the advent of television.

5 Write the 2 **ous** words in section 2 which are synonyms
(words that mean the same).

More about -ous

1 Some adjectives end **-ious** or **-eous**. Try reading these words with your teacher.

hideous   furious   serious   spontaneous   envious   curious

various   glorious   mysterious   miscellaneous   previous

Some end **-uous**
sumptuous   contemptuous   deciduous

2 Match these words with their meanings.

spontaneous	assorted
simultaneous	easy to understand
courteous	mistaken
instantaneous	unplanned
obvious	at once
miscellaneous	lacking respect
contemptuous	at the same time
erroneous	polite

3 Underline **-ous**. You should find 12.

The carnivorous animal was not concerned about either coniferous or deciduous trees. All it wanted was marvellous meat. The villagers were nervous of it. They stopped arguing about trees and started a vigorous campaign to get rid of the mysterious beast. They became quite famous for a time as news of their struggle against the night-time predator, thought to be an enormous tiger, reached the outside world. Then the animal disappeared and they went back to their ridiculous divisions over the planting of new coniferous or deciduous trees.

4 Baby snake:

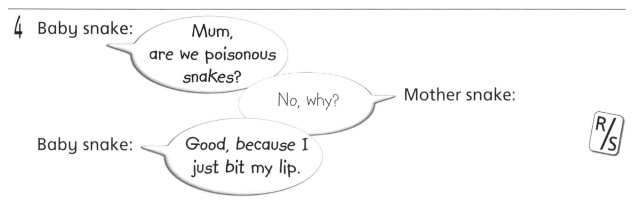

Mum, are we poisonous snakes?

No, why?   Mother snake:

Baby snake: Good, because I just bit my lip.

R/S

75. Reading comprehension: searching for key points

1 📖 Read and underline or highlight the key points about why mobile phones are useful in modern society.

I think I can persuade you to agree with me that mobile phones are a blessing to modern society.

They are handy, compact in size and very lightweight, so they are easy to carry around. Some people keep them in their bags, but most have their phones concealed in a pocket. That way it is easy to answer a call quickly and it's also more difficult for pick-pockets to steal them. For most people carrying a phone is now as natural as getting dressed. It would be hard to forget to take it, like forgetting to put on your shoes.

Having your mobile phone with you means you can contact anyone anytime, even if they are on the other side of the world. On a day-to-day basis they help us to arrange meetings and appointments. If you are running late you can easily let your friends know. If you are lost, you can phone for directions.

Obviously a mobile phone is invaluable in an emergency. There's no frantic searching for a phone-box. The emergency services can be summoned immediately, saving crucial minutes, if not hours, when someone is injured.

There's no need to worry if you've forgotten to take your calculator, camera, clock, alarm clock or MP3 player. The latest mobiles have all these features built into that tiny little plastic device that fits so neatly into your pocket.

You don't have to pay a fortune for one of these little miracles of modern science. A basic phone for talking and texting is well within most people's price range. It isn't necessary to have all the latest technology on your phone. Just being in touch in this way is affordable and certainly worth every penny.

Buying a phone is very straightforward. There are plenty of specialist shops in the high street or you can buy a phone over the internet. You can even pick up a mobile phone in your local supermarket.

If you are the sort of person who doesn't like talking on the phone, then there is the texting facility. You can send typed messages by using the letter buttons on your phone.

2 Use the list of key points you have made to write your own short piece about the advantages of mobile phones.

Consonant digraph CH ch *ch*

1 Say **chemist**

The <u>ch</u>emist has a cure for stoma<u>ch</u> a<u>ch</u>e.

2 Underline **ch**. Split these words into syllables and read to your teacher.

e.g. or|chid   charisma   chronic   chaos   cholera

      echo   lichen   bronchitis   chronicle   melancholy

      chord   character   chlorine   chasm   mechanic

3 Read these words. Match them to the clues to fill the grid.

chlorophyll   cholesterol   chrysalis
chromosome   chronological

1 Events arranged in order
   of their occurrence.
2 Structure in cell which
   carries genetic information.
3 Green pigment in plants
   responsible for light absorption.
4 Too much in the blood supply can
   lead to heart disease.
5 Caterpillar's form whilst changing
   into a butterfly or moth.

4 Underline or highlight **ch**. You should find 10.

The schooner slipped anchor and slid smoothly past the dusty wharves
with their crumbling architecture and on towards the open sea.

Despite his charisma, a carefully planned scheme to restore the exiled
monarch had failed once again, and there was a strong sense of
melancholy aboard the boat as she sailed out towards a setting sun.
A final blast from the ship's horn echoed around the channel as this
noble character stood at the stern, regarding for the last time his small
country, which was now on the brink of chaos.

77. Reading -ti -ci -ssi -xi **in words**

1 [RULE 📏] In words of more than 1 syllable **-ti, -ci, -ssi, -xi** say [sh 🔊] when followed by a vowel.

Underline **ti ci ssi xi** in the following words.
Split them into syllables and read.

e.g. pro|vin|cial [sh 🔊]   pa|tience [sh 🔊]   superficial   crucial   ferocious

commercial   ancient   malicious   auspicious   procession

position   suspicious   facial   efficient   cautious

torrential   officious   passion   superstitious   special

noxious   sufficient   permission   influential   patient

2 Trace and add *ous*.

pretenti_____
delici_____
infecti_____
preci_____
graci_____
vici_____
anxi_____

Trace and add *al*.

palati_____
spaci_____
offici_____
marti_____
initi_____
soci_____
essenti_____

3 [📖] **-ti** and **-ci** say [sh 🔊].

The bump**ti**ous politi**ci**an was famous for his large appetite. He was espe**ci**ally par**ti**al to the deli**ci**ous meals which an ambi**ti**ous chef sometimes provided for him, unoffi**ci**ally. He had a passion for a certain deli**ci**ous pudding and was known to eat more than an elegant suffi**ci**ency at times. He would show his appre**ci**ation by making a generous finan**ci**al dona**ti**on to the management of this provin**ci**al residen**ti**al hotel.

4 Listening comprehension. Note the key points. Track 37.

Choosing a better word

Using words in an interesting way.

1 Substitute an appropriate adjective from the list
below to use instead of the overworked **nice** or **nicer**.

large well-scrubbed fresh tasty stiff friendly smart
fine refreshing strong bright sticky interesting
short restless waterproof thick tangy red more
pleasant huge well-filled sparkling healthy
wonderful new

It was a *nice* _____ day for the long-awaited Sea Rangers' outing to the coast.
Twenty-five excited teenagers gathered on the platform of Central Station to wait
for the train to Southend. After much preparation they were armed with a *nice*
_____ hamper, a *nice* _____ itinerary and some spending money.

After a *nice* _____ train ride they found themselves hurrying to the docks to
board their *nice* _____ clipper ship. It had a *nice* _____ coat of paint
and *nice* _____ canvas sails flapping gently in the *nice* _____ breeze.

Everyone scrambled aboard excitedly and jostled for a place on the *nice* _____
deck. The luggage was soon stowed away and the skipper gave them their
instructions in a *nice* _____ voice. They were soon heading for the open sea.

Luckily there was hardly a cloud in sight. The sails billowed eagerly in the *nice*
_____ wind and it wasn't long before the hull began to pitch and roll on the
threatening waves. They were glad that they had brought their *nice* _____
anoraks and their *nice* _____ sweaters as they were soon covered in the
salty spray.

One or two began to feel queasy and to look distinctly pale. Luckily the wind had
dropped by lunch time and the weather became much *nicer* _____. All had
nice _____ appetising treats: roast chicken, sliced ham, fresh bread rolls and
salad for the main dish. This was followed by *nice* _____ pineapple slices and
nice _____ cream. They quenched their considerable thirst on *nice* _____
orange or lemon drinks. Little did they know, at that stage, what lay ahead.

2 Write an exciting account of what happened next.
Plan it using a spider diagram. Think carefully about the words you use.

79. Using prefixes and suffixes to change meaning

1 Split into **root word**, **prefix** and **suffix**.

	Prefix	Root word	Suffix
replacement			
disgraceful			
unluckily			
beloved			
adventurer			
explainable			
preconditions			
indistinctness			
confirming			

2 Use these prefixes to change the meanings of these words.

com   dis   ex   il   im   in   re   un

___sane	___frequent	___equality	___considerable	___claim
___human	___certain	___legal	___similar	___proper
___perfect	___aware	___popular	___patient	___continue
___press	___approve	___probable	___current	___necessary
___obedient	___usual	___change	___spire	___pose

3 Turn these nouns into adjectives by adding a suffix.
Remember the spelling rules.

-ic   -ful   -al   -ive   -ous

	Noun	Adjective	
e.g.	a metal	metallic___	sound
	a skill	___	craftsman
	an effect	___	remedy
	an athlete	___	man
	an expense	___	car
	a mercy	___	release
	an accident	___	death
	a poison	___	plant
	a faith	___	dog

Long-vowel pattern EI ei *ei*

Colour the long-vowel pattern <u>red</u>.

1 Say **ceiling** .
The sound is
the same as
alphabetical name E.

K**ei**th paints the c**ei**ling.

---

2 ei after letter c says .

receipt deceive conceit perceive receive
Remember the spelling rhyme:
i before **e** except after **c**.

3 ei E))).

caffeine protein
seize heinous
counterfeit

4

In the hurly-burly of the rush hour at Kings Cross Station, Paul Floyd searched anxiously for his elderly aunt, a pensioner, who was arriving for her autumn visit on the 18.32 from Thurso in the north.

At last he spotted his loyal relation struggling under the weight of a ridiculously heavy case. He dropped his new briefcase and surged forward with the crowd to greet her.

He kissed her awkwardly. As they walked up the platform arm in arm, happy to be in each other's company again, Paul remembered his briefcase.

It won't surprise you to learn that the briefcase had vanished and with it many important papers connected with his work as a lawyer at Lloyd, Phillips and Matthew. Paul left his aunt and went to find or phone a policeman. He soon found one. In fact he found several. There was great excitement and commotion outside the station as police were keeping people away from an army mechanic who was in the middle of the road fiddling with a technical device which he was attaching to a new briefcase.

"I want to report a missing briefcase." Paul mumbled nervously to a policeman with a moustache who looked like the chief officer there. "I think a thief purloined it!"

His words were drowned by a loud explosion. Tiny pieces of blue leather blew sky high and charred papers began to drift down.

"And can you give me a description of this briefcase?"

"It's blue leather," muttered Paul.

A sign above his head read; "Unattended luggage will be confiscated."

What do you think happened next? Use a spider diagram to note your ideas and then write your own continuation of the story. Remember to use paragraphs.

5

81. Consonant digraph CH ch *ch*

1 Say **chef** [sh].

The **ch**ef sips **ch**ampagne.

2 Underline **ch**. Read with your teacher.

e.g. <u>ch</u>ivalry ma<u>ch</u>ine bro<u>ch</u>ure
  <u>ch</u>auffeur <u>ch</u>alet avalan<u>ch</u>e
  mousta<u>ch</u>e <u>ch</u>ute para<u>ch</u>ute
  <u>ch</u>iffon <u>ch</u>evron <u>ch</u>icanery

3 Read the words in the boxes and use them to complete the sentences.

ch [k]	ch [sh]	ch [ch]
Christmas	chalets	choosing
orchestra	brochure	checking
choir	avalanche	challenge
architect	chauvinists	
technical	parachuting	
school	Charlotte	

1 The _____ and _____ were _____
  carols for the _____ concert.

2 The ski holiday _____ did not mention that the
  _____ were close to the site of last year's _____.

3 The _____ was _____ his _____
  drawings for the new _____.

4 _____ found herself amongst a group of male _____
  when she took up the _____ of _____ as a hobby.

4 Copy the headings into your exercise book and write the words you hear in the correct column using neat joined-up writing. Track 38.

ch [k]   ch [sh]   ch [ch]

5

What's the difference between a wet day and a lion with a toothache?

One pours with rain and the other roars with pain?

R/S

Essential spellings

1 Work across. ⟶

Read	Trace, naming letters	Write
1 special	*special*	
2 receive	*receive*	
3 except	*except*	
4 minute	*minute*	
5 actually	*actually*	
6 suitable	*suitable*	
7 science	*science*	
8 machine	*machine*	
9 caught	*caught*	
10 naturally	*naturally*	

83. Proofreading

This account was written by a dyslexic boy on return from Cub camp. It is going to be printed in the Cub newsletter and it is your job to write it out correctly before printing.

- Listen to your teacher reading the account and underline all spelling mistakes.
- Correct the spelling mistakes and add missing commas, full stops and capital letters.
- Mark the end of the paragraphs like this //. A paragraph is a group of sentences about the same topic or idea. It starts on a new line.
- Write or type the corrected version, dividing it into three paragraphs.
- Compare your proofreading with the version in the teacher's notes on page xvi–xvii.

e.g.

breakfast   packed our   our   destination

after <u>brefast</u> we <u>packt</u> <u>are</u> bags and went to <u>are</u> next <u>desterneshon</u> which was two miuls away. Our cub leder said it woud tack us one houer to get there but we thurt it would tack longer and we sat of. It did onley tack us one houer when we reached are desterneshon we pich are tents quily so we had time to go for a walk wich we did not like but we made a deul that if we went for a walk we could have a camp firere that night. The walk was not to long and we got are bages for walking tow miuls and at lest we had someone to tuke to it was nerly tow oklok so we had some lunch we did do some archarey and afletics closely supavised until five oklok we had a bit of a shock at five oklok because a sponserd walk came righght thuw were are tents were pichid so we have to move are tents. Bay the time we moved are tents it was gating dark and we had a camp firer and the cub leder got some march malos we cookt them on the bon fier then we had a game of football in the dark then we protendid to gow to slep. wen the cub leder had gon we snuk out and got up to some mifchif. We got back into are tents an hoer or sow later then we gust torkt for the rest of the night.

Regular final syllable -TURE -ture -*ture*

1 Say **vulture** chər)).

Try to cap**ture** the vul**ture**.

2 Trace, adding the syllable *ture*, and read.

mix   *adven*   *sculp*   *tex*

frac   *scrip*   *depar*   *punc*

na   *lec*   *fix*   *pic*   *fu*

tor   *agricul*   *vul*   *cap*

3 Choose from the words in section 2 to find the correct answers
and then write your own clues for the rest.

An ugly scavenger

Has not happened yet

To do with farming

You would get one if you broke a bone

Book about God

Shaped out of stone or metal

Say 'goodbye' before this

It's a shame to _____ wild animals

Something exciting or dangerous happens

You like to taste this when someone is baking

Plants, animals, weather, wildlife

A sporting event

4 Jason, a fanatic, keeps his vulture in THE attic.
It perches in the rafters all day long.
At feeding time its antics are in every way quite frantic.
As it tries to gulp the crickets down in one.

Read the following passage and answer all the questions, using your own words as often as possible. Remember to obey instructions carefully and to present your answers neatly. Write in complete sentences and take care with spelling and punctuation.

In 1915 Sir Edward Shackleton, certainly one of the most heroic adventurers of the 20th Century, set off in his ship, the Endurance, for Antarctica. Antarctica is the icy area around the South Pole in the southern hemisphere. His intention was to be the first man to walk across Antarctica.

However, as the wooden square-rigged ship made her approach to the base camp, the sea began to freeze around her and she was soon trapped in ice, which was forming around the ship. The crew first lived on board the ice-bound ship, hoping that they could survive until the following spring when the ice would start to melt. It soon became clear that they would have to set up camp in the snow as the ship was in danger of cracking up under pressure from the increasing ice. No sooner had they removed their vital supplies from the ship than she did crack up totally and disappeared beneath the surface. It must have been a terrifying moment when she finally went down and they were left with no means of transport home.

Sir Edward Shackleton's dreams of walking across Antarctica were shattered. From now on his **prime** concern was to get all his men home safely to Britain. To do this he had to keep their morale high and to convince them that it was possible. He made a plan to walk over the ice to the water's edge and then sail to the nearest land, at Paulet Island. They set off on a **gruelling** journey, hauling the big wooden life-boats with them. They made slow progress but eventually got to the edge of the ice and put to sea in two life-boats. They sailed 312 miles, but the wind took them past their destination and onto Elephant Island instead. The men were **ecstatic** to find themselves on dry land again, but their happiness was short lived when they realised that the island was uninhabited.

Shackleton made the decision to sail onwards in one of the boats to South Georgia, where there was a whaling station and help. He took five men with him and left his deputy in charge of keeping spirits up amongst his men, some of whom were beginning to despair.

After sixteen terrible days in the stormy seas of the South Atlantic, Shackleton and his five men sighted South Georgia, only now they were in danger of being wrecked on the rocks. By some miracle they were carried on past the rocks and eventually made a landfall. By now three of the men were very weak and sick. Then they discovered they were on the wrong side of the island from the whaling station and a high mountain range separated them.

Shackleton set off with the two other fit men to climb the mountain range. They were mightily relieved when they heard the siren waking the men at the whaling station at 7 a.m.. It was the first sign of human life they had experienced for over a year.

After a period of recovery, they took a rescue ship back to Elephant Island and after four months they rescued all twenty-two of the men. The deputy had kept the men's spirits up by telling them every day for four months that they must pack up and be ready to move because Shackleton might be back.

The entire rescue had taken eighteen months by the time Shackleton and his crew returned to England in 1917.

---

1 What is Antarctica? (1 mark)

2 Why did the crew move off the ship and set up camp in the snow? (1 mark)

3 What is the name of the island the crew first escaped to? (1 mark)

4 Shackleton took five men with him to get help. What dangers did they face in doing this? (4 marks)

5 How many men were rescued? (1 mark)

6 How did Shackleton's deputy keep the men's spirits up whilst they waited on Elephant Island? (4 marks)

7 What evidence is there in the passage to suggest that Shackleton was a remarkable man? (4 marks)

8 Re-read the sentences that include the words in bold print (**prime, gruelling, ecstatic**) and say what you think the author means by these words. (3 marks)

87. Reading and writing to complete the story

1

My story begins on 31 October. I had to take a pizza to Bridge Cottage. When I got to the place written on the piece of paper, it looked like it was abandoned. I knocked on the old oak door, but no one came. I knocked again and I was about to go when a faint voice said, "Who's there?"

I said, "The pizza man."

A little boy answered the door. He asked, "How much is it, please?"

I answered in a surprised voice, "£10.50. That includes garlic bread and two pizzas at £5.50 and one free coke. Then a hamburger and chips for £5.00 and then another free coke, thank you."

I thought that was a lot for a small boy who did not look even thirteen years old, but I had to give it to him because he had ordered it and I did not want to lose my job over this.

Back at the office Hussein, another pizza man, who deals with the wages, told me that a little boy of twelve had run away from a local foster home. He had taken an excessive amount of money from the other children and from the safe.

By now it was twelve at night and I did not want to go back to the house in the dark, so I decided to go in the morning.

I woke up in the small hours, still thinking about the boy. I had a picture of him in my head, all alone in the house. I looked at my watch. It was 2.30 a.m.. There were some questions I wanted to ask, so I decided to return to the cottage as soon as it got light.

2 What do you think happened next? Use a spider diagram to note your ideas and then write your own continuation of the story in your exercise book. Remember to divide your writing into paragraphs. When you have finished, proofread your work, checking for spelling mistakes, punctuation and words you may have left out or written in the wrong order.

How much have you learned?

1 Punctuation. Write this short passage in your exercise book, being careful to include all punctuation.

It was my brothers birthday last week he was given some felt tips two books a computer game a cricket bat and a new bike he wont let anyone ride his bike i cant say i blame him i let cameron ride mine and he managed to twist the back wheel when he landed in a ditch on his way to dorchester hes not allowed to ride a bike now so he has to borrow bens scooter do you think this is fair

2 Parts of speech. In the following sentences underline the part of speech named.

Noun
He sat under the table for three hours.

Adjective
Her green dress was torn as she scrambled over the fence.

Conjunction
He was eating a banana while he was watching television.

Adverb
Dad was cleaning the car carefully.

Verb
John climbed Mount Kenya when he was in Africa.

Preposition
The cow jumped over the moon.

3 Dictionary. All the words in the following two lists have the same first three letters. Arrange them in dictionary order in your exercise book according to their fourth letters.

1 decide   decoy   decrease   decay   declaim   deck   decent
2 consult   conceal   condition   confess   convoy   contest   conical

Look up these words in your dictionary.
Underline the word which is not an animal.

coypu   coyote   hoyden

4 (Sp) Ask your teacher for a spelling test.

89. Can you read these multi-syllabic words?

dangerous	electronic	character	energetic
receive	supersonic	machine	audience
nervous	perfection	announcing	sensible
circulation	disturbing	appointment	dispatching
royalty	retriever	responsible	automatic
awkward	nephew	embroidery	continue
weighing	basically	microphone	incredible
anxious	residue	neighbourly	jewellery
audible	believable	mountaineer	atmosphere

Self-assessment checklist

What have you learned? What do you need to revise?
Give yourself a mark out of 10 for each of these skills.
You may need to ask your teacher to help you fill this in.

Spelling

Sound–letter relationships (R/s) ☐
Long-vowel spelling patterns ☐
Essential spellings ☐
Adding suffixes to silent e words ☐
Adding suffixes and doubling ☐
Plurals ☐
Sequencing and spelling the days of the week ☐
Sequencing and spelling the months of the year ☐

Writing

The alphabet ☐
Joined-up handwriting ☐
Good sentence structure ☐
Writing a postcard ☐
Writing from picture prompts ☐
Planning a story ☐
Writing an imaginative story ☐
Writing from your own experience ☐
Writing a summary ☐
Proofreading your own writing ☐

Punctuation

Correct use of capital letters ☐
Correct use of full stops and question marks ☐
Use of commas ☐
Use of speech marks ☐
Use of 's ☐
Contractions ☐

Reading

Recognising short-vowel sounds ☐
Recognising long-vowel sounds ☐
Reading 1-syllable words ☐
Reading 2-syllable words ☐
Reading 3 and 3 + syllable words ☐
Understanding a short passage ☐
Understanding a more complex piece ☐
Reading and noting key points ☐
Reading aloud to other people ☐
Using a dictionary ☐

Grammar

Knowing what a noun is ☐
verb ☐
adjective ☐
adverb ☐
preposition ☐
conjunction ☐

Listening skills

Detecting rhyming patterns in words ☐
Hearing different vowel sounds in words ☐
Hearing consonant sounds in words ☐
Remembering lists ☐
Following instructions ☐
Taking notes ☐

Certificate of Merit

Presented to

_____

for the successful completion of

Beat Dyslexia Book 5

Signed _____ (Teacher)

Date _____

Practice sheet for handwriting